THE CHILDHOOD OF FAMOUS AMERICANS SERIES

By CHARLOTTA M. BEBENROTH
Meriwether Lewis: Boy Explorer

By BERNICE BRYANT
Dan Morgan: Boy of the Wilderness

By CONSTANCE BUEL BURNETT
Lucretia Mott: Girl of Old Nantucket

By OLIVE W. BURT
Luther Burbank: Boy Wizard
John Wanamaker: Boy Merchant
Young Jed Smith: Westering Boy
The Ringling Brothers: Circus Boys

By ELECTA CLARK
Robert Peary: Boy of the North

By CHRISTINE NOBLE GOVAN
Rachel Jackson: Tennessee Girl

By SUE GUTHRIDGE
Tom Edison: Boy Inventor

By MARIE HAMMONTREE
Will and Charlie Mayo: Doctor's Boys
A. P. Giannini: Boy of San Francisco

By MARGUERITE HENRY
Robert Fulton: Boy Craftsman

By HELEN BOYD HIGGINS
Alec Hamilton: The Little Lion
Stephen Foster: Boy Minstrel
Juliette Low: Girl Scout
Walter Reed: Boy Who Wanted to Know

By JANE MOORE HOWE
Amelia Earhart: Kansas Girl

By LAURA LONG
Oliver Hazard Perry: Boy of the Sea
David Farragut: Boy Midshipman
George Dewey: Vermont Boy

By MIRIAM E. MASON
Mark Twain: Boy of Old Missouri
Young Audubon: Boy Naturalist

By MIRIAM E. MASON—cont.
William Penn: Friendly Boy
Mary Mapes Dodge: Jolly Girl
Dan Beard: Boy Scout
Kate Douglas Wiggin:
   The Little Schoolteacher

By GRACE HATHAWAY MELIN
Maria Mitchell: Girl Astronomer

By MINNIE BELLE MITCHELL
Hoosier Boy: James Whitcomb Riley

By HELEN ALBEE MONSELL
Boy of Old Virginia: Robert E. Lee
Tom Jefferson: A Boy in Colonial Days
Young Stonewall: Tom Jackson
Dolly Madison: Quaker Girl
Henry Clay: Mill Boy of the Slashes
John Marshall: Boy of Young America
Woodrow Wilson: Boy President
Susan Anthony: Girl Who Dared

By AILEEN WELLS PARKS
Davy Crockett: Young Rifleman
Bedford Forrest: Boy on Horseback
James Oglethorpe: Young Defender

By EDD WINFIELD PARKS
Teddy Roosevelt: All-Round Boy

By HOWARD PECKHAM
William Henry Harrison: Young Tippecanoe
Nathanael Greene: Independent Boy

By MARIAN T. PLACE
Lotta Crabtree: Girl of the Gold Rush

By ALEXANDER SCHARBACH
Boy Sailor: Matthew Calbraith Perry

By FLORA WARREN SEYMOUR
Bird Girl: Sacagawea
Pocahontas: Brave Girl

...continued on next page

THE CHILDHOOD OF FAMOUS AMERICANS SERIES—Continued

By BRADFORD SMITH

William Bradford: Pilgrim Boy
Dan Webster: Union Boy
Stephen Decatur: Gallant Boy

By DOROTHEA J. SNOW

Eli Whitney: Boy Mechanic
John Paul Jones: Salt-Water Boy
Raphael Semmes: Tidewater Boy
Samuel Morse: Inquisitive Boy

By WILLIAM O. STEELE

John Sevier: Pioneer Boy
Francis Marion: Young Swamp Fox

By AUGUSTA STEVENSON

Abe Lincoln: Frontier Boy
Ben Franklin: Printer's Boy
Andy Jackson: Boy Soldier
George Washington: Boy Leader
Daniel Boone: Boy Hunter
Sam Houston: Boy Chieftain
George Carver: Boy Scientist
Kit Carson: Boy Trapper
Paul Revere: Boy of Old Boston
Clara Barton: Girl Nurse
U. S. Grant: Young Horseman
Buffalo Bill: Boy of the Plains
Anthony Wayne: Daring Boy
Myles Standish: Adventurous Boy
Booker T. Washington: Ambitious Boy
Wilbur and Orville Wright: Boys with Wings
Molly Pitcher: Girl Patriot
Zeb Pike: Boy Traveler
Nancy Hanks: Kentucky Girl
Tecumseh: Shawnee Boy
Sitting Bull: Dakota Boy
Virginia Dare: Mystery Girl

By GUERNSEY VAN RIPER, JR.

Lou Gehrig: Boy of the Sand Lots
Will Rogers: Young Cowboy
Knute Rockne: Young Athlete
Babe Ruth: Baseball Boy

By GUERNSEY VAN RIPER, JR.—cont.

Jim Thorpe: Indian Athlete
Richard Byrd:
  Boy Who Braved the Unknown

By JEAN BROWN WAGONER

Lousia Alcott: Girl of Old Boston
Jane Addams: Little Lame Girl
Julia Ward Howe: Girl of Old New York
Martha Washington: Girl of Old Virginia
Abigail Adams: A Girl of Colonial Days
Jessie Frémont: Girl of Capitol Hill

By ANN SPENCE WARNER

Narcissa Whitman: Pioneer Girl

By ANN WEIL

John Quincy Adams: Boy Patriot
Franklin Roosevelt:
  Boy of the Four Freedoms
Betsy Ross: Girl of Old Philadelphia

By MABEL CLELAND WIDDEMER

Washington Irving: Boy of Old New York
Aleck Bell: Ingenious Boy
Harriet Beecher Stowe: Connecticut Girl
Peter Stuyvesant: Boy with Wooden Shoes

By KATHERINE E. WILKIE

Zack Taylor: Young Rough and Ready
Will Clark: Boy in Buckskins
Mary Todd Lincoln: Girl of the Bluegrass
George Rogers Clark:
  Boy of the Old Northwest

By ELLEN WILSON

Ernie Pyle: Boy from Back Home
Annie Oakley: Little Sure Shot

By GERTRUDE HECKER WINDERS

James Fenimore Cooper:
  Leatherstocking Boy
Jim Bowie: Boy with a Hunting Knife
Ethan Allen: Green Mountain Boy
Jim Bridger: Mountain Boy

THE
RINGLING
BROTHERS
Circus Boys

by

OLIVE W. BURT

Illustrated by
RAYMOND BURNS

THE BOBBS-MERRILL COMPANY, INC.

Publishers

INDIANAPOLIS   NEW YORK

To

DAVID HAND

a very special boy

The Circus!—The Circus!—The
   throb of the drums,
And the blare of the horns, as the
   Band-wagon comes;
The clash and the clang of the cymbals
   that beat,
As the glittering pageant winds down
   the long street! . . .

JAMES WHITCOMB RILEY,
The Circus Parade

CONTENTS

CHAPTER   PAGE

    I   The Circus Comes to Town   13

   II   Circus Magic   38

  III   The Great Panorama Show   54

  IV   A Menagerie Begins   77

   V   Music in the Air   90

  VI   A New Home   105

 VII   The Menagerie Grows   120

VIII   The Town Takes Notice   133

  IX   The Brothers Organize   165

   X   Circus Kings of America   182

THE RINGLING BROTHERS

Circus Boys

I

THE CIRCUS COMES TO TOWN

1. *Elephants and Bareback Riders*

"Look, Alf T., look! Look, Otto! It's the circus at last!"

Six-year-old Charles Ringling dashed ahead of his brothers. He ran to where a man was nailing posters on the wall of his father's little harness shop. He stared up at the brightly colored pictures.

Alf T. and Otto came up beside Charles. They began to read the words that stood in big red letters above the pictures. Three-year-old Johnny trotted up to stare with open mouth at the gay figures on the posters.

"Look at the horse!" Johnny said, pointing.

It was a warm Saturday morning in the summer of 1869. The four brothers had just brought

13

Papa Ringling's lunch to him. Mama Ringling had told them to hurry back home, but they could not pass up the man who was tacking the posters to the wall. They had waited so long for the circus! Ever since their big brother Albert had told them that a circus would come to town this summer, they had talked about it.

The boys looked so much alike that anyone could tell they were brothers. All had dark brown, wavy hair, dark eyes and round, rosy cheeks. Now Otto, eleven, and Alf T., eight, were so busy spelling out the words on the posters they had forgotten Charles and Johnny.

Alfred's middle name was Tanner. Everyone called him "Alf T.," because it didn't sound quite so much like Albert, his big brother's name.

"What does it say, Alf T.?" Charles asked.

The man answered Charles. He had his mouth full of tacks, so his words came out only one side of his lips.

"It says Dan Rice's Circus is coming to town, that's what it says, Bub!"

At the man's feet lay a bundle of posters with colored pictures of clowns, acrobats and animals. These had been rolled together. There was a strap with a handle to hold them together, so they could be easily carried. The man stooped. He peeled off another sheet from the roll and held it against the wall. From his mouth he took a tack with a little square bit of leather under the head. With a small hammer he tacked the sheet to the wall.

"Why do you put leather on your tacks, Mister?" Charles asked. Charles talked to everyone and everyone seemed to like him.

This man did. He grinned down at the little boy. "So the wind can't tear the dodger down. You see, when the wind blows, the paper might pull away over the tack head. But the leather holds it fast, so it doesn't tear."

Now Alf T. had a question. "What's a dodger?"

"These are dodgers," the man explained, pointing to the posters. "Circus dodgers. I travel ahead of the circus and nail these up so folks will know when the circus is coming."

"What's that, Charlie?" Johnny asked, pointing.

"That's an elephant, silly. When is the circus coming, Mister?"

"Next Tuesday. You going to see it?"

Charles nodded. Of course they were going!

Otto was carefully reading out loud the words on the dodgers. " 'Dan Rice's Great Paris Panoramic Circus! Coming! Coming!' "

"I know what a panorama is!" Alf T. boasted. "We had one at school. It's a lot of pictures that show different places and things." He stopped and thought. Then he asked, "The circus isn't going to be just pictures is it?"

The man laughed. "Nope. That's just Dan

"Will all those things be here?"

Rice's way of saying there's going to be lots of costumes and animals."

Charles pointed to the dodgers. "Will all those things be here? Elephants—real elephants? And horses and—?"

"Bareback riders?" Alf T. interrupted. "Our big brother Albert used to try to ride standing up on a horse like that."

"But he fell off!" Otto said, snickering.

The man stooped, rolled up the unused dodgers and fastened the strap. Then he turned to his horse, which had been standing patiently while his master worked. The man put the dodgers into a huge saddlebag, and stepped up into the saddle.

"You boys keep your ears open. Then you'll hear the circus boat when it comes up the river. It's got one of those new steam organs. Makes a lot of noise. You'll hear it!"

He jerked on the reins and started off down the dusty road. As he went he rang a large bell and shouted, "Ladies and Gents! Ladies and Gents! Dan Rice's Circus is coming!"

The brothers watched till he was hidden by the cloud of dust from his horse's hoofs. Then they turned and looked at the river, as if they might see the circus boat that very minute.

The little town of McGregor, Iowa, lay high on the western bank of the Mississippi River. Just outside town the ground sloped sharply to the water's edge, and there was a wooden dock. The boys of the town loved to go down to the dock to watch the river boats.

"We'd better get along home," Otto said. "Mama said to hurry back."

The three smaller boys started obediently down the road, toward the little house where the Ringling family lived. But Charles could not bear to walk. He had good news for his big brother. He wanted to be the one to tell it first. He dashed ahead, his bare feet kicking up almost as much dust as the circus man's horse had done.

"Wait for me! Wait for me, Charlie!" cried Johnny.

Charles could not hear him. Charles was singing, "Ladies and Gents! Ladies and Gents! The circus is coming! Elephants and horses and lions and tigers!"

When he reached his own yard he saw Albert and Gus, the two oldest boys. They were coming from the garden. Usually these two big boys helped Papa in the harness shop. But recently there had been little work to do there. The garden was important, too, because it furnished a great deal of the family's food. And the garden needed weeding and hoeing. So Albert, seventeen, and Gus, fifteen, had spent the morning at this work.

When Charles saw Albert he let out a whoop. "Guess what! Guess what!" he shouted. "The circus is coming next Tuesday, Al!"

Albert stopped in his tracks. "Are you sure, Charlie?" he asked. "I've been waiting to hear about it."

"I know! I know! I saw the dodgers. With elephants and lions and tigers——"

Albert put out a hand and ruffled Charles' mop of dark hair. "Hold on there, Mister!" he said, chuckling. "I don't think Dan Rice has all those animals."

"Well, he has elephants and bareback riders, anyway!"

Gus wiped his shirt sleeve across his sweaty forehead. "That'll be a great day for Mc-Gregor!" he said crossly.

Albert smiled and said good-naturedly, "You don't have to go, Gus. You can stay home and weed the garden."

"Oh, I'll go! Everybody'll go! Just because I don't play circus like a little kid is no sign I don't want to see a real circus."

Albert's face grew serious. "I guess it does seem like child's play to you, Gus. But it's serious for me. For someday, as sure as I'm standing here, I'm going to be a circus performer."

"Albert's going to be a circus rider!" Charles said stoutly.

Just then the other boys came up. Otto and Alf T. each had hold of one of Johnny's hands and they dragged the little fellow along as they hurried. His fat legs churned up and down, making a cloud of dust.

Charles turned toward Otto. "We're going to see the circus! Even Gus is going to see the circus!"

Otto looked up at his oldest brother. His face was serious. "How much will it cost?" he asked soberly.

Albert shook his head. "Trust Otto to think of the cost!" He stopped there, for he knew that they didn't have money to spend on things they didn't need. Papa Ringling's harness shop did a fairly good business. But with a big family of boys to feed and clothe there was never anything left over for foolishness.

"Well, anyway," Albert said cheerfully, "we can go down to the river and watch the boat come in. We can see everything when the boat docks."

"And we can see the parade, too. It's free!" Otto declared. "The parade's the best of all."

They all hurried into the house to tell Mama Ringling about the circus.

2. *The Circus Boat*

It was still dark on Tuesday morning when Albert awakened his brothers.

"Come on, boys! Get up. It's time to go down to the dock if we want to see the boat come in."

They needed no coaxing. Even Johnny climbed out of bed, rubbing his eyes. They pulled on their homespun pants and shirts.

"Are we going to take Henry?" Charles asked Albert.

His big brother shook his head. "Henry's just a baby. He wouldn't understand."

Down the road toward the river the six brothers hurried in the soft darkness of the early summer morning. The dust was cool to their bare feet.

The Ringling brothers were not alone on the road that morning. Other boys were up, too, and hurrying down to the dock. There were even a few men, moving like tall shadows through the gray light. The smaller boys had a hard time keeping up with Albert's long legs. Johnny stumbled as he ran. Albert turned. He scooped up his little brother and placed him on his shoulder. Charles ran, panting a little, at Albert's side.

Charles had been thinking about Albert and the circus. Now he looked up at his big brother and asked, "Are you going to get a job with Dan Rice's Circus, Al?"

Albert answered ruefully, "I wish I could. But I'm not ready yet. Dan Rice wouldn't have me."

"I think you are good enough," Charles said

stoutly. "You can *almost* ride standing up on a horse!"

Gus laughed. "Almost isn't good enough. You forget that Albert fell off when he tried that trick on Old Gray."

"Nick Bruhn joined the circus that came last summer——" Charles began.

"But that wasn't Dan Rice's Circus! Dan's is the best in the whole country. He has only the best performers," Albert explained.

The other men and boys were crowding down to the dock. "Let's go over there," Albert suggested, pointing to a little rise of land close by the dock. "We can see better from there."

Suddenly a shrill sound pierced the morning air. It sent little shivers up Charles' spine. He leaned forward, turning his face to the south. He tried to see around the bend in the river. He held his breath, listening, while the high, screeching music filled him with excitement. Now the boys could recognize the tune.

"Oh, Susanna! Oh, don't you cry for me,
    For I come from Alabama with my
        banjo on my knee!"

Alf T. began to sing the words. Johnny pranced in time to the music. He never could keep his feet still when a lively tune was being played.

Albert cried, "There she is!" They all leaned forward as far as they dared. Johnny almost toppled over, but Albert grabbed his shirttail and held onto the little boy.

There it was—the circus boat! It came around the bend in the river. Rosin torches were burning on the deck. They flared and wavered in the river breeze. It gave the boat a magical look. From the smokestack came billows of black smoke. The music kept playing, high and shrill.

Charles watched in silence. The boat moved slowly, proudly up the river. It came even with the dock and stopped.

Charles turned to Alf T. "Look at the people!" he whispered excitedly. "See them there on the deck!"

Alf T. nodded.

The music stopped. Bells clanged. Shouts and yells rose from the boat. The vessel was eased close to the dock. A man stood at the rail, holding high a flaring rosin torch to give light for the docking.

"What's that behind the boat?" Charles asked, pointing.

"That's the barge with the wagons and trunks and tent poles and tents," Albert explained. "The people and animals travel on the boat. But most of their equipment is carried on the barge towed behind."

As the boat touched the dock, the little crowd of watchers called out, "Hello, the boat!"

A small, elegant man, dressed in a handsome dark suit and wearing a tall, stovepipe hat, came to the rail. Someone in the crowd said, "There's Dan Rice!"

"Hurrah for Dan Rice!" Albert cried. The crowd took up the shout, "Hurrah for Dan Rice!" Charles cheered so loudly his throat hurt.

A gangplank was lowered from the deck to the shore. First the troupe left the boat. Then the barge was unloaded. Four spotted ponies were led ashore; then a dozen dogs on leashes.

At last a great, gray animal stepped onto the gangplank. It walked carefully down to the dock. It was the first time an elephant had ever come to McGregor, but even Johnny recognized it at once. He remembered the picture on the dodger.

"Elephant!" he shouted, clapping his chubby hands. "See the elephant, Charlie!"

The huge beast stepped from the dock to the

ground. He placed his big, clumsy-looking feet neatly. His small, amber eyes looked out from heavy folds of rough, gray skin. His long, wrinkled trunk waved slowly to and fro. Johnny crowded close to Albert. Charles was watching every move the elephant made.

Behind the elephant came a group of women, chattering as they hurried along. Men, animals and women crossed the dock and went up the road toward the meadow south of town. That was where the circus tents would be pitched.

Albert looked down at his brothers. "Well, what do you think of it?"

Gus answered, "It's the best part of the circus. We get to see the animals and people close up. We can see they are *real,* not make-believe. The circus is too make-believe for me!"

"Of course the circus animals and people are real," Albert agreed. "Most of the circus performers are from small towns like ours. You remember Nick Bruhn. Well, he was real, wasn't he? But I like the performance best, because then the people *don't* seem or act like us. In the circus everything is changed to magic. . . ."

Albert's voice trailed off. He knew he couldn't make Gus see what he meant. Gus never joined in the make-believe games and stories of his brothers. He had no patience with Albert's practicing to ride bareback, or to juggle Mama's plates on his finger, or to walk a tightrope.

"The parade's magic, too," Otto said. "We can go and see that."

"We'd better hurry, then," Albert advised.

The Ringlings walked faster. Their home was at the northern edge of town. They'd barely have time to get home, eat their breakfast and do their chores before time for the parade.

3. *The Parade*

The Ringling boys were lined along the sidewalk in front of Papa's harness shop before the parade left the circus grounds. Mama and Papa were still inside the shop. They promised to come out just as soon as they heard the music of the band. Papa said he would hold baby Henry up so he could see.

Charles was glad they had the shade of the harness shop to stand in. Outside the shade, the sun beat down bright and hot. He turned to look up at Papa's sign over the door: AUGUST RINGLING —HARNESS MAKER

Charles could not remember when the sign had been changed, but he knew that it used to say "August Rüngling." But when Papa and Mama had become American citizens they had changed the German name to an American one —Ringling.

"I'm glad Mama came," Charles said, brushing an unruly lock of hair out of his eyes.

"Of course she came!" Otto exclaimed, jingling the pennies in his pocket. Otto always seemed to have two or three pennies to jingle. "No one stays home from the parade!"

Gus wasn't with his brothers.

"Gus is lucky!" Charles said. "He'll probably get a free ticket to the show."

"Yes," Albert agreed enviously. "I tried to get a job like Gus's, carrying water for the animals, but they said I was too old. Anyway, Gus is always better at getting jobs than I am. He'll probably sell his ticket. He'd rather have the money than see the show. But he likes working with the animals."

"Maybe he'll get to pat the elephant," Charles said, his eyes bright with the thought.

From where they stood, the boys could see the white top of the big tent. Bright red and yellow and blue pennants were flying in the sun.

At last there was a stir in the meadow. A bugle blared. Charles grabbed Johnny's hand and held it tight. Excitement pounded through him.

A man came riding up the street on a white horse. He shouted, "Make way! Make way! The circus is coming!"

Other children had come to stand in the shade of Papa's shop. Mike and Chad Hood were there. They were friends of Alf T. and Otto. Charles moved to make room for Aaron Koss and his little sister, Anna. Aaron was Charles' best friend next to his own brothers. Papa and Mama came out of the shop to watch. Papa held little Henry on his shoulder. All down the street, men and women and children stood, leaning forward, watching.

Dan Rice rode at the head of the parade. He sat on a large black horse, with red ribbons on its mane and tail. He held his silk hat in his hand and bowed right and left, smiling. The crowd clapped and shouted. "Hurrah for Dan Rice!"

The spotted ponies came next. They were

Dan Rice rode at the head of the parade.

pulling the band wagon. They stepped high and, like Dan Rice, nodded their heads right and left. The red and blue plumes on their bridles bobbed up and down. The band was playing Charles' favorite tune:

"Turkey in the straw! Turkey in the straw!
   Roll 'em up and twist 'em in a high tuck-away!"

The band wagon was followed by the trained dogs, hitched to a tiny cart. The cart was driven by a man with a chalked face and a peaked hat.

"Look, Mama!" Johnny shouted, pointing.

"The man is bigger than the cart!" Charles laughed.

"He's crying, Mama! Why is he crying?" Johnny asked.

"He's just fooling, Johnny," Charles explained. "He's a clown, and clowns do everything to make you laugh."

"Elephant!" Johnny pointed his chubby finger.

"He's all dressed up now," Charles said. "Is that gold, Albert, real gold on his blanket?"

"It looks like gold." Albert smiled down at the little boy. "That's Dan's wife in the howdah —the seat on the elephant's back."

"Is she scared?" Charles asked, breathless at the sight of the beautiful lady up there so high.

"Of course not, silly!" Otto answered, impatient at his younger brother's questions.

More clowns followed the elephant. They were dressed in bright suits and their faces were painted. They tumbled along in the road. They tripped over their enormous shoes. The children shouted with amusement.

A crowd of boys tagged along behind the clowns, teasing them, poking fun.

"I'm going with them!" Charles cried, and ran into the street.

Otto and Alf T. started after their brother. But Mama Ringling said, "No! No! Boys, you stay here with us. Running in the street like that is not good."

Charles stopped where he was, in the middle of the street. From farther and farther away came the music of the band. Its gay, marching tune seemed to be saying, "Come, Charles, come!"

But he turned back to join his family.

II

CIRCUS MAGIC

1. *A Bit of Good Luck*

THE Ringling family turned away from the street that seemed so empty now. Everyone was moving and talking. Some were going toward the meadow; others were starting homeward. The Ringlings went into Papa's harness shop.

Papa set baby Henry down on the work bench and turned to his other sons. "It was a fine parade, no?" he asked.

Charles stood at one side. He brushed a lock of hair out of his eyes. He thought hard. Then he made up his mind. He went to his father.

"Can't we see the circus, Papa?" he begged.

Papa Ringling shook his head sadly. "It costs too much. I am sorry, boys." They could tell by his voice that he was really sorry.

"Come, boys!" Mama said briskly. "It is time now to go home. Work is there to be done. You, too, Papa. Come home and have a good dinner. You will then forget the circus, yes?"

Just then a young man came into the shop. The boys turned to look at him. He seemed a stranger to them. He must be one of the circus performers, Charles thought. He wore a wide, heavy leather belt and a bright shirt.

"Howdy, Mr. Ringling," the young man said.

Papa stared at the fellow. Then a smile broke across his ruddy face. He held out his hand. "Nicholas Bruhn!" he cried. "My, how you have changed in the year! And how goes it with you, eh? So big and strong you are!"

Nicholas chuckled. "Yes, I've grown some, I guess, and put some real muscles on my arms." He held up his arm, his fist clenched, and flexed his muscles.

The boys gathered around him and watched, their eyes wide with admiration.

Nicholas went on: "I have to be strong for my job. I figured out a good circus act—juggling a cannon ball. So I left the show I went away with last summer. It was small potatoes! And I joined Dan Rice."

"Is it hard to get a job with Dan Rice?" Albert asked eagerly.

"Hi, Albert!" Nicholas turned. He grinned and held out his hand. "Are you still hankering to be a circus performer? I remember your stunts well—especially your attempt to ride that old gray horse standing up on his back. Well—" he shrugged—"the only thing to do is to work up a new stunt. Then take your chances, the way I did."

He turned to Papa Ringling. "Look what happened. The socket that holds the pole on which I balance the cannon ball, here on my belt, is broken. I thought of you at once. Can you mend it right away?"

Papa Ringling examined the leather socket that hung down in front of the wide belt. *"Ja,"* he said, nodding. "Yes—this I can do with ease." He took the belt and went to work.

Nicholas turned to Albert. "I'll tell you how it is, Al," he said in a friendly voice. "There's always room for a good performer with a new trick. But it's a hard life, traveling all the time. Are you sure that's what you really want to do?"

"Oh, yes, I'm sure!" Albert answered. "I've been sure ever since I saw my first circus. That was back in Milwaukee, before we ever came to McGregor. I was only a little fellow like Johnny here—three years old, I guess."

"Our Albert, he just seemed to go crazy about that circus!" Mama said, shaking her head a little sadly. "To understand why, I have often tried. No one in our families was ever a circus man. I do not like to think of our Albert in a circus. I keep the hope that his mind will change."

"It never will," Albert said firmly. "No other life seems at all exciting or good to me."

Charles listened eagerly. When Albert said this, he nodded his head and grinned. Albert would be a circus rider yet. And he might find a place for his brothers, too!

Papa Ringling came back with the mended socket. "Here is the belt, Nick. Just as good as new. Better even!"

Nicholas examined the socket and smiled. "That's fine, Mr. Ringling. How much do I owe you?"

Papa smiled and shrugged. "Nothing. For my old neighbor I do it with gladness."

The listening boys sighed and glanced at one another. If only Papa would charge him, maybe some of them could get to the circus.

Nicholas chuckled. "Same old Mr. Ringling! Doing things for free when you have the least excuse. You'd be rich, sir, if you charged like other people."

He reached into his pocket and took out a small yellow square of cardboard. With the stub of a pencil he wrote on the little card. He held it out to Papa.

"Anyway, here's a pass to the circus—for the whole family. Just hand it in at the ticket window——" He turned and hurried out of the shop.

The boys crowded around Papa. Charles stood on tiptoe to see. He stared at the magic yellow card. Johnny didn't know what it was all about, but he knew something special was happening. He bent over, put his hands on the floor and turned a somersault.

As his heels flew over his head they struck the wooden tub of water in which Papa soaked the leather he was working on. The tub stood on a small stool. When Johnny's feet hit it, stool and tub went over with a crash. The water flooded the floor. Johnny was soaked. But he came up laughing.

His heels struck the tub of water.

Mama picked Johnny up. "Come, boys!" she said. "Come, Papa! We must get this clown into some dry clothes. Everybody clean up the floor. Then you boys have some dinner before you go to the circus, no?"

Albert glanced soberly at Papa. "Except for mopping up this floor none of us will do a bit of work today. Is that all right, Papa?"

"Mama and I will stay home and look after things." Papa chuckled. "One day in the summer is circus day. Well, a holiday it should be, I think."

Charles clapped his hands. "Of course Dan Rice day is a holiday!"

2. *Under the Big Top*

Six Ringlings were waiting at the ticket wagon long before circus time that afternoon. Gus had joined his brothers when he learned that the pass was good for all of them. And he had not sold the ticket he had earned carrying water to the animals. At the last minute, Gus had seen Charles' chum, Aaron, standing beside the ticket wagon. Aaron was looking sadly at the people in line waiting to purchase tickets.

"Here, Aaron," he said. "Here's a ticket. You come on in with Charlie."

Charles felt like hugging Gus, right there before all that crowd. But he knew Gus wouldn't like that. So he just reached out and patted his brother's leg to show how pleased he was.

Albert handed the yellow pass up to the ticket man and was given a pink ticket for each of them. He herded his brothers and Aaron through the crowd and into the big tent.

Charles stared about him. "Look how big it is!" he exclaimed.

"We have to sit on the blues," Albert said, turning toward one side of the tent.

"Those are the cheap seats," Gus explained to the younger boys. "See, they're painted blue. But they're just as good as the reserved section."

Albert had read everything he could about circuses. He loved to use circus words. Now he said, "It looks as if Dan's going to have them on the straw."

Since Gus had been working around the tents all morning, he felt like an old circus hand. He told the boys, "Al means there's going to be such a crowd that some will have to sit on straw in front of the first row of seats. Maybe Dan will have bales brought in to sit on. Looks as though he'll have to."

The big tent was filling up. The people pushed and crowded. Some climbed from row to row so they could sit high up, near the very roof of the tent. Others rushed to get seats in the front row.

"Let's sit here," Charles begged, "so we'll be closer to the animals and clowns."

Albert nodded, and they squirmed into the small space not already taken by others.

Charles sniffed. His nose twitched with the smell of straw and people and animals and sawdust. "Smell!" he said to Alf T. "It smells good, doesn't it?"

"It smells circusy," Alf T. answered.

Charles couldn't hear him above the racket. In fact Charles didn't try to hear him. Charles' head was bobbing this way and that, trying to see everything.

He turned to Aaron. But he didn't say anything. Aaron, too, was trying to see everything at once. There was no need for talk right now.

Suddenly through the smells and the dust and the noise there came a new sound—the clear, golden notes of a bugle. *"Ta-tatatata! Taa! Taa! Tatatata!"*

The crowd became silent. Everyone looked toward the end of the tent.

The band marched in, playing a tune that made prickles run up and down Charles' back. Alf T. and Otto tapped their feet in time to the stirring air.

Around the sawdust ring marched the band. Then came Dan Rice, the ringmaster. He looked elegant in white trousers and a black, swallow-tailed coat. He carried a long whip.

He was followed by the horses. They now wore bright silk blankets and colored plumes on their bridles. They stepped high, turning this way and that, prancing, dancing with the music. Beautiful ladies sat on their backs, holding the reins so tight that the horses' necks were arched and their heads high and nodding.

Charles thought they must be the most beautiful horses in the world. If Albert couldn't stand on the broad back of their work horse, Old Gray, what a time he'd have on one of these!

The spotted ponies danced in. They lifted their tiny hoofs daintily. They nodded their beautiful little heads. Their forelocks hung down over saucy eyes that seemed to laugh at the crowd.

Even the elephant tried to keep time to the music as he marched clumsily around the ring, his trunk waving slowly from side to side.

Charles reached out and took hold of Albert's arm. He knew now how his big brother felt about the circus. It was the only place to be— here in this world of action and fun and gay music and bright colors.

After the elephants came the clowns, tumbling close to the first row of seats. They stumbled and tripped over one another. They cried and laughed and pulled faces. One had a big lollipop which he offered to the children on the first row. Johnny shrank back, afraid, but Charles laughed and made a grab for the candy. The clown leaped away, fell and rolled in the sawdust. The children near Charles shrieked with laughter and clapped their hands.

When all the performers had marched around the ring, the real circus began. Men and women in spangled tights swung from trapeze bars high against the dim top of the tent. Bareback riders flashed around the ring. Nicholas Bruhn stood in the center of the circle, balancing a heavy cannon ball on one end of a long pole held in the socket Papa Ringling had mended.

"Look, Al!" whispered Charles. "There's a man who can juggle four plates at once. Watch him, Al. See how he does it?"

The real circus began.

"Ponies! Ponies!" Johnny was pointing. He
stood up and shrieked, "Don't hit 'em!"

Otto and Alf T. pulled Johnny back to his

seat. "Be still!" Otto ordered. "Dan Rice doesn't whip the ponies. He just snaps the whip. They mind the crack of it. Be still and watch."

"Look at the elephant, Johnny," Charles said. "Now he's kneeling down. Now he's lying down. And now he's rolling over!"

One circus act followed another. Then, all too soon, the show was over. The performers gathered in the center of the ring. They stood still, each one in his place, to make a pretty picture. In front of them Dan Rice bowed to right and left. The band played "Home, Sweet Home." The bugle blew. The performers kissed their hands to the audience. Then they ran out of the ring and disappeared.

Noise filled the tent—noise and dust and smells. The people climbed down from their seats and moved toward the entrance. Charles reached for Albert's hand. His brother looked down at him and smiled.

"Let's have a circus of our own, Al!" Charles said eagerly. "You could juggle as well as that man if you tried. We could all do something. When will you start your circus, Al? *When?* I can't wait!"

Albert squeezed his hand. "Well, we will do something about that," he promised.

III

THE GREAT PANORAMA SHOW

1. *Getting Ready*

THE younger Ringling boys could talk of
nothing but the Dan Rice Circus, and the
circus they wanted to have themselves.

Each one had a different idea.

Otto wanted their production to make money.
"Anyway, it should bring in *something*," he said.

Alf T. was sure that if they put some bright
dodgers around town, they'd make the show pay.

Charles' mind was full of thoughts of stunts
and animal acts.

Johnny was turning somersaults all over the
place. He had the notion that he would be the
top performer, no matter what the other boys
decided.

Albert and Gus were taking no part in these
plans. Both of the older boys were busy at Papa's

shop. Papa Ringling had just received an order from a store in Prairie du Chien, across the river, for seven harnesses in a hurry. Papa and Gus and Albert were working day and night to fill this order.

One day Charles slipped down from his chair at the dinner table and went to stand close to Albert.

"Now what are you after?" Albert asked good-naturedly.

"Help us, Al. Help us give a circus."

Albert ran his fingers through Charles' thick hair. "I'd like to help, Charlie. But I haven't any time right now. Why are you in such a hurry?"

"It's the right time—exactly right!" Otto put in. "Don't you see, Al? Everyone in McGregor is still talking about Dan Rice's Circus. Some of the boys and girls didn't get to see it. If we have one, they'll try to come."

"Old businessman Otto!" Albert chuckled. He thought for a minute and then said seriously, "Look here, boys. A circus takes more time and money than you have. A circus needs animals and trained performers. Why don't you settle for some other kind of show? Maybe a concert. You all play some instrument."

"Not very well!" Alf T. said gloomily.

"Well, a panorama show, then."

Otto and Alf T. looked at each other. Charles frowned. He did so want a real circus!

"Maybe a panorama show would do," Otto said slowly. "But we'd need a machine to show the pictures." He began to get excited over the idea. "You remember, Alf T., what it was like? The man had pictures painted on canvas. The pictures showed places he had traveled—New York City and Washington and everywhere. And the canvas was wound on rollers, and he talked about each picture. We *could* do that!"

"And we could make dodgers and nail them up on Papa's shop! And go through the town yelling about it the way that man did."

"You see?" Albert said, pushing back his chair and getting up to go back to the shop. "You see, you can have fun without having a circus."

Charles followed Albert to the door. "I'd rather have a circus," he insisted.

Albert laughed down at him. "You get to work with the others and you'll soon forget that circus business."

Charles didn't say anything, but he thought, "You don't forget it, Al. And I won't forget it either!"

Albert turned back. "Listen, Otto. You boys get your scenes painted and everything ready. Then I'll help you make your panorama machine tonight."

That set the boys going. They left the table and went out to the barn loft.

"Let's see what we have to work with," Otto suggested, as they climbed the ladder to the loft.

Up in the loft they all started looking for things to use. Charles spied two rolls of wallpaper Papa had given them when he finished papering the parlor last spring. He lugged them out to the middle of the floor. "Can we paint the pictures on these?" he asked. "On the back, I mean, where there are no flowers."

"Just the thing!" Alf T. said, his usually low voice loud now with excitement.

"And look!" Otto cried. "Here are some pink pasteboard boxes that Papa had. We can cut them up to make tickets."

"We can use those scraps of wallpaper for dodgers," Alf T. said, pointing to some on the floor. "Then we won't have to cut into the big rolls. It's lucky we saved every piece."

Charles had been scouting in every corner. He came out with two nearly empty cans of paint.

"Here's the paint Mr. Koss gave us for running errands, when he was making those new signs for his bakery."

Otto dropped to the floor, laughing. "We saved everything—even though we had no idea what to do with it. We won't have to worry about the show! Let's get right to work."

Johnny had been quietly busy by himself. Now he dipped a brush into a paint can and started to make a picture on the roll of wallpaper.

Charles caught his hand just in time. "Wait, Johnny!"

Otto said quickly, "Look, Johnny, we'll give you some paper of your very own that you can paint pictures on."

"Will you put it in the show?"

"We'll see." Otto, being the oldest of the four, took charge. "I'll make tickets. Alf T., you paint dodgers. Charlie, you start cleaning up so the loft will be ready."

"Aw, shucks!" Charles grumbled. "That's not fair! I don't want to do the dirty work. You'll have all the fun. After all, I was the one who found the paint. I can paint better pictures than you or Alf T. You know that."

"Well," Otto said, "you take some of those scraps and try your hand. Show us how good you are. Maybe you'll do all right." He walked away, jingling his pennies.

"Ho! Ho! Ho!" Johnny shouted. He bent over and put his hands on the floor to turn a somersault.

Charles grabbed him and sat on him. "No, no, Johnny! You might kick our paint over. You know what happened at Papa's shop."

Johnny got up, put his thumb in his mouth and looked as if he were going to cry.

"Look," Alf T. said gently, bending over his little brother. "You go down and practice on the lawn. It's nice and soft there. And if you're good, we'll let you have a part in the show."

Johnny's sunny smile came back. "All right, Alf T.!"

Otto nodded approvingly. "Good for you, Johnny. Now we can work in peace."

2. *The Machine*

The boys could hardly wait till after supper to show Albert and Gus what they had done that afternoon. The big boys were amazed.

"Who painted all the pictures?" Albert asked, staring down at the rolls of wallpaper. They were covered with scenes from *Robinson Crusoe, Tom Thumb* and other favorite stories.

"I did most of them!" Charles boasted proudly.

"We all helped—even Johnny," Alf T. added in his quiet voice. "I guess some of my pictures look pretty funny. But at least you can tell what they are pictures of."

"Well, it looks as if you mean business," Al-

"Who painted all the pictures?"

bert said. "Gus and I have talked this over today. He's going to help me build your panorama machine. I believe we've worked it out. But you boys had better leave us alone up here to do it. You know Mama always says too many cooks spoil the soup."

They hated to leave, but they knew Albert. When he said for them to do something, he meant it. So they climbed down the ladder and hurried with their evening chores.

The boys came back to the house to find Albert and Gus sitting on the porch.

"Did you make it?" they asked, all shouting together.

"Yes, it's done. But you'll have to wait till tomorrow—when it's daylight—to see it."

They were all up early and out to the loft. Albert and Gus were already there.

"Behold the great original panorama machine!" Albert cried, waving his hand toward the contraption.

The boys crowded around to examine it. Charles dragged over an empty barrel and climbed up on it so he could see better. Albert hoisted Johnny to his shoulder.

On two wooden sawhorses, Albert and Gus had placed a long, wooden packing case in which some of Papa's tools had come. The front had been taken off. In its place, stretched tight across the opening, was the wallpaper with the picture of Robinson Crusoe showing.

Gus took hold of a flat piece of wood at the top of the box, close to one end. He turned this in a circle, and the wallpaper began to move. In a moment the picture of Robinson's man Friday appeared.

"That's just the thing!" Otto exclaimed enthusiastically. "But how—?"

"Look! We cut away a little section of each end, here at the front of the box. Then we made rollers from these old broken spade handles. We made holes in the top of the box—one at each end —and stuck the ends of the roller up through those holes. The flat wooden handle acts as a crank."

"Keep rolling, Gus! Keep rolling!" Charles cried.

Gus kept rolling, and the pictures on the paper appeared and disappeared like magic.

"We nailed each end of the roll of paper to the wooden rollers," Albert explained. "We took good care to keep the picture side out."

"What do we do when it's all rolled up onto this roller?" Alf T. asked, pointing.

"Then you go over to the other end. The roller is fixed the same way, and you can roll it back again. You have to do that before your show starts."

Otto was thoughtfully jingling the pennies in his pocket. He was thinking. Now he said, "But we have two rolls of paper covered with pictures. How will we show the other roll?"

"You'll just have to nail it on the rollers. Take this roll off and nail that one in its place."

"That will take time."

Albert looked at Otto. "Can't you figure out how to handle that?"

"I know! I know!" Charles chanted. "Johnny can turn somersaults and sing that funny song while we change the pictures."

Albert reached over and ruffled Charles' hair. "There's our showman!" he declared. "Otto, you should listen to Charlie. He is an idea man for you."

Otto frowned. Idea man! Charles was Albert's favorite and everything he did was fine with Albert. Well, I have ideas, too! Otto thought. Where would they be without *my* ideas to make the show pay?

"What are you going to charge for admission?" Gus asked.

"A penny each!" Otto declared.

"That's pretty steep for your first show, isn't it?"

"That's what I told him," Alf T. said. "I think

it's important to get a crowd. And lots of the boys and girls don't have pennies to spend." He glanced at Otto's pocket. "If we just charge pins —everyone can get a few pins from his mother. The crowd would help advertise our next show."

"Alf T.'s right, Otto," Albert agreed. "Don't scare your crowd away by charging too much."

Then it occurred to Otto that if they got enough pins they might sell them to Mrs. Druber, the dressmaker, for a few cents.

"Oh, all right!" he said grudgingly. His face brightened. "Will you write the story to go with the pictures, Al? Please?"

Charles jumped down from the barrel and ran to his big brother. "Please, Al! You tell the best stories."

Albert was flattered. "I'll think up something. But it's going to be hard to work all those pictures into the same story."

3. *Trouble in the Loft*

By Saturday afternoon everything was ready. Alf T. had taken the dodgers downtown and nailed them up on fences and on the walls of Papa's shop. Albert had written the story and Otto had memorized it.

Alf T. was to turn the crank that operated the panorama machine.

Charles was to help Alf T., and he would play a tune on his mouth organ while the picture rolls were being changed. Johnny had learned his funny song to perfection. Everything was ready.

Otto stood at the foot of the loft ladder selling tickets. He was trying to attract a crowd by shouting, "Come one, come all! See the Ringling Brothers' Show! The great panorama show! Only ten pins!"

Many boys and girls came. Otto counted them

as they lined up for tickets—nineteen, twenty, twenty-one.

Each one gave Otto ten pins and was handed one of the tickets he had made from the pink pasteboard boxes. On the tickets was printed in pencil:

ADMIT ONE
RINGLING BROTHERS' GREAT NEW
PANORAMA SHOW

The children climbed the ladder to the loft and handed their tickets to Alf T. He was ticket-taker until it came time to run the machine. The audience found places on the seats the boys had made. They had put boards across the tops of empty kegs and boxes. Some of the children sat on sacks of grain or bales of hay.

When the last child had climbed to the loft, Otto gathered up his box of pins and hurried up to join them.

"I'll stand here in the back and see if everything goes all right," Otto decided.

He looked over the audience. All their friends and acquaintances seemed to be there, from little Anna Koss, only four years old, to Griff Bennett and Jode Crowell, two big fellows who often bullied the smaller boys. Otto frowned. He wished they hadn't come.

Charles was to open the show. He had practiced his speech over and over. Albert had helped him get the words and tone right. Now he stepped to the front of the audience and began in a loud, showman's voice: "Ladies and Gents! You are about to see the greatest and best show of its kind in the entire city of McGregor, Iowa! If you will kindly pay attention, the show will begin. Our first pictures present the great and famous story of *Robinson Crusoe!*"

He bowed low, and the children clapped and stamped their feet. Griff Bennett yelled, "Come on! Don't talk so much! Show us the pictures!"

Otto nodded to Alf T. He began to turn the crank. The pictures rolled out. Otto came forward and began to tell the story as Albert had written it.

The first picture showed a rather wild-looking man in a brown, furry suit.

Otto said, "This is Robinson Crusoe, who once upon a time went down the river on a flat boat."

Alf T. turned the crank. A new painting appeared. It was a picture of a man in a boat.

"This, as you see, is Robinson in his boat. Robinson always spat on his bait, so he always had good luck. One day he caught so many catfish that the boat got overloaded. Before it sank, he put a keg of nails in his pocket and a saw between his teeth, took a hammer in one hand and an ax in the other. He shouldered his trusty gun. You can see it all in the picture, of course.

Then he swam to shore, and that proves what a peach of a swimmer he was!"

The little children giggled and clapped at the silly story.

But Griff Bennett hooted. "This is a rotten show! That ain't the story of Robinson Crusoe! It ain't anything. I never saw such awful pictures. I want my pins back!"

"Yes! It's a rotten show!" bawled out Griff's chum, Jode. "Give our pins back!"

Otto looked at the trouble-makers in disgust. "Your pins were bent and rusty," he declared.

"They were not!" bellowed Griff.

"They were so!" shouted Otto.

"Call me a liar, will you? Well, I'll make you eat your words!" Griff started toward Otto with Jode at his heels. Two other bullies, Ben Crum and Jack Cooper, joined them.

Alf T. let go of the panorama crank. Mike and Chad Hood rushed toward Otto and Alf T. The other children stood up and cried, "Throw

The trouble-makers were greatly outnumbered.

them out! Throw them out! We want to see the
show!"

They gathered around the four bullies and
pushed and pulled at them. The trouble-makers
were greatly outnumbered. Before long they
found themselves at the head of the ladder. It

was all they could do to get down safely, the others pushed and crowded so.

"Here are your pins," Otto said. "Divide them up fair and square." He held out a handful of bent, rusty pins. Ben Crum grabbed them and followed his friends.

The other children went back, straightened their seats, and watched quietly through the rest of the show.

Johnny's song, during the change of rolls, was the big hit of the afternoon. The little boy had a good voice and could carry a tune well. And he loved to show off, so he sang with a great deal of expression and with many funny faces:

"Old Dan Tucker was a mighty man.
He washed his face in a frying pan.
He combed his hair with a wagon wheel,
And danced with the toothache in his heel!

"Hurrah for Old Dan Tucker!
He's too late to get his supper!"

The children clapped and stamped and shouted. Johnny had to sing his song over again.

4. *A Real Clem!*

As soon as he got home that evening Al asked, "How did the great panorama show go?"

"We had a fight," Otto said. "We had to throw Griff Bennett and his crowd out."

Albert laughed. "So you had a clem! That's what real circus people call a fight like that. Did you shout, 'Hey, Rube'?"

"What's that, Al?" Alf T. asked.

"Well, usually when a circus goes to a small town there are some rough fellows who want to make trouble. They try to get in without paying, or want their money back, or something. So when the fight starts, the circus men yell, 'Hey, Rube!' Then all the roustabouts—the men who put up the tents—come running. They soon put an end to the trouble-makers. And that kind of a fight is a clem."

"Well, we had a clem! A real clem!" Charles said, grinning.

"It's good practice for the time when you will have a real circus!" Albert declared.

Mama Ringling frowned. "Fights is it yet? For my good boys fights and yelling. Are you then going to be rowdies and not gentlemen?"

"Maybe we can have a gentlemen's clem!" Charles giggled. His brothers looked at him, and then everyone began to laugh.

IV

A MENAGERIE BEGINS

1. *A Naughty Goat*

IT was a hot summer day a whole year after the great panorama show. The four younger Ringlings were walking down the dusty Mc-Gregor street, pulling their little express wagon heaped with cabbages. They were taking them to Mrs. Druber on the other side of town.

This summer the garden had been turned over to Otto and Alf T., with Charles and Johnny to help. The boys had worked so hard and had been such good gardeners that they often had extra vegetables to sell. This helped with the family expenses, and the boys had more pocket money than ever before.

"Look, Otto!" Charles shouted. "There's that old billy goat eating the clothes on Mrs. Bennett's line. Looks as if he's chewing up Griff's long winter underwear."

The boys stopped and looked into the Bennetts' yard. Sure enough, there was the livery-stable goat chewing away at an arm of a union suit.

"I wonder why she's washing them in the summertime," Alf T. said. He knew that his mother packed their winter underwear away when spring came.

"Maybe she found some moths in them," Otto suggested. "But we shouldn't let Billy eat them up." He ran toward the fence. "Get out of there, Billy!"

Billy went on chewing calmly. He paid no attention to the boys. He was used to people shouting at him. He was in trouble most of the time. But trouble didn't bother Billy.

Just then Mrs. Bennett looked out her kitchen window. She saw what Billy was doing. She came rushing out the kitchen door, waving a broom and crying, "Get out of there, you pesky critter!" She swung the broom and gave Billy a smack on the back.

Billy cocked a saucy eye at her. He threw back his head. His ragged beard waved in the air. Then he gave a last tug at the underwear. The clothespins flew from the line. Away Billy went. He dashed through the open gate, the underwear arm still between his teeth. The garment trailed behind in the dust.

Mrs. Bennett ran after the goat. "Give me back that union suit!" she called, trying to hit Billy with the broom.

The boys liked Mrs. Bennett, but they couldn't help laughing. As Billy went leaping past them, Otto let go of the wagon and took after him. He caught up with Billy and dragged the underwear from his teeth. One arm was practically gone, but Otto came back with what was left of the garment.

"Give me back those things!"

"Here you are, Mrs. Bennett," he said politely. He managed to keep from grinning.

"That pesky critter!" Mrs. Bennett cried angrily. "He ought to be penned up, that's what! I'm going to make Jack Winter over at the livery stable pay for this underwear!"

She marched rapidly down the road toward the livery stable. Otto picked up the wagon tongue and the four boys followed her at a distance.

Charles took hold of Otto's sleeve. "Listen, Otto, if Old Jack gets mad at Billy, maybe he'll give him to us."

"What would we do with him?" Otto asked.

"We could teach him tricks!" Charles said.

"We could start a menagerie," Alf T. added in his quiet voice. "Then, when we have a circus, we'd have a real trained animal for it."

"Well, we haven't got him yet," Otto said.

At the livery stable Mrs. Bennett and the stable man were having an argument.

Old Jack scratched his head, frowning. "I don't feel called upon to pay for everything that old goat does," he grumbled.

"Well, somebody's going to pay!" Mrs. Bennett insisted.

"You see," Jack argued, "he don't rightly belong to me. He just hangs around and I feed him. Can't bear to see him go hungry."

Mrs. Bennett was determined. "This suit of underwear cost a good fifty cents. And it was just like new, too. Now it's ruined. I want the cost of it, Jack Winter, and I'm going to stand right here till I get it."

Charles whispered to Otto, "Let's give her the money, Otto. Then Billy would be ours for sure!"

"Have we got fifty cents?" Alf T. asked.

Otto didn't answer. He wasn't jingling his pennies now. Charles looked at Alf T. They shook their heads sadly at each other.

"I've got eight cents at home," Alf T. said at last.

"I've got five cents. How much have you got, Johnny?" Charles asked.

"I've got a penny, a penny, a penny!" Johnny chanted.

Charles and Alfred turned to look at Otto. They knew he had money. He always had. Otto stared back, frowning. At last he said slowly, "You all have fourteen cents. If I put up the rest, thirty-six cents, the goat would be about three fourths mine and just one fourth yours. I'd be his boss. Is that right?"

Alf T. was about to nod agreement. But Charles let out a howl. "That's not fair! I saw Billy first. I said let's buy him. I ought to be boss."

"Idea man!" Otto said scornfully. "Just because Albert thinks you're so smart is no reason for you to be boss of anything. You're only seven! I'm the oldest. I'll have to put in the most money."

Alf T. said reasonably, "I don't think you have enough to buy him by yourself, Otto. You need our help. And, as Charlie said, it really was his idea."

"I want to be boss, too!" Johnny wailed.

"Why don't we all put in what we have and then all own it. Share and share alike. We can't expect Johnny to have as much money as the rest of us," Alf T. suggested.

They stood looking at one another in silence. Then Mrs. Bennett's shrill voice came again. "How long do you expect me to stand here, Jack Winter? I want my money."

Otto stepped forward. "Excuse me, Mr. Jack. Look, Mrs. Bennett. We haven't got the money with us right now, but if you'll let us have Billy for our very own, we'll pay for the underwear."

"That would be a blessing!" Mrs. Bennett frowned. "But how do I know you'll bring me the money?"

"Just take our word for it, Mrs. Bennett. We'll bring it without fail," Otto promised. "Will you let us have him, Mr. Jack?"

"Of course I will. He's no good to me—or to anybody else so far as I know."

"Is Billy ours, then?" Charles asked eagerly.

"He sure is," Mr. Jack said.

Now the job was to catch Billy. He stood a short distance away and watched the boys warily as they tried to sneak up on him.

"He's laughing at us!" Charles cried.

They moved slowly toward the goat from different directions. When they closed in, almost near enough to grab him, Billy tossed his ragged beard in the air and bounded away. He went fast, his head down, his broken horns thrust forward. Otto and Alf T. flung themselves headlong at the animal. They collided and went down. Instead of butting them, Billy tried to jump over them. But their arms shot up and each grabbed a handful of his long, tangled hair.

"We've got him!" Otto shouted.

Old Jack came running with a rope and helped the boys tie it around Billy's neck. "Can you get him home?" he asked anxiously.

"We'll get him home," Otto said. "Charlie, you help me. Alf T. and Johnny can deliver the cabbages."

2. *Billy Rainbow*

Mama Ringling came to the door as Otto and Charles dragged Billy into the yard. "What is that you have there, eh?" she asked. Then she saw what it was and cried, "No! No! That dirty goat does not come here to live."

"Oh, Mama," Charles said, "he's ours! We bought him."

"We're going to start a menagerie, Mama," Otto explained.

"A menagerie yet! With that dirty creature?" Mama was upset.

"We'll take care of him, Mama," Charles promised. "We're going to wash him and brush him. And we'll save our spending money to buy food for him. He won't bother anybody, Mama."

"Let us try it, Mama. Please!" Otto begged.

Mama looked at the two boys standing there with such anxious faces. "Oh, you boys!" She sighed. "Well, if you must have him, I suppose you must."

"Thank you, Mama," Otto said happily and led the goat out to the barn.

Charles ran to Mama and threw his arms about her waist. "You're a peach, Mama!" he said.

Alf T. and Johnny soon returned from delivering the cabbages. They had hurried as fast as they could. They handed the money from Mrs. Druber to Mama and ran out to the barn. There all four boys spent the rest of the afternoon, feeding Billy, washing him, brushing his tangled hair and rubbing ointment into the sores where dogs had bitten him. They had a time of it getting him to stand still while they worked on him.

When Papa and Albert and Gus returned from the harness shop, they went out to take a look at Billy. The older Ringlings chuckled when they saw the boys' pet.

They spent the rest of the afternoon washing Billy.

"So pretty you make him!" Papa said, patting Johnny's curly head. "Billy Goat is not a nice enough name for such a beautiful creature."

The boys knew Papa was joking. Billy was still rather raggedy-looking and thin.

"We'll think up a better name for him," Alf T. said slowly.

Charles had tied Billy's forelock with strips

of old cloth to keep it out of his eyes. The goat's hair had been wet and the cloth had faded. Streaks of red, green and blue had run down his face. Now Billy cocked his yellow eyes up at Charles and shook his head.

Suddenly Charles began to laugh. "Look at Billy! Look at Billy! He looks like a rainbow."

"That will all wash off," Otto said. Then his eyes lighted up. "Rainbow. Say, that's the name for him—Rainbow."

"Billy Rainbow! Billy Rainbow!" Charles clapped his hands.

"Yes," Papa agreed, "that is for him a very good name."

V

MUSIC IN THE AIR

1. *When Blizzards Blow*

CHARLES, Alf T. and Otto burst into the kitchen with a shout. Snow and wind came with them. They pulled off stocking caps and mittens, shaking the snow from them.

"It's a regular Iowa blizzard, Mama," Otto said. "We had a hard time getting home from school."

"Warm yourselves a bit," Mama Ringling advised, "and then do your chores before dark. Plenty of wood we'll need tonight for the stoves. In the parlor, too, a fire we must have. You remember? Tonight is the night for music lessons. You are lucky Papa can trade work for the lessons."

"Mr. Walter won't be coming tonight,

Mama," Alf T. said. "The wind would blow him and his horn right into the Mississippi."

Charles giggled. "*Onto* the Mississippi, you mean, Alf T. The river is frozen solid."

Johnny was struggling with his heavy overshoes.

"Where are you going?" Charles asked.

"To help you feed Billy Rainbow."

"You can't. You're too little." Charles reached down to take away the overshoes.

Johnny clung to them. They scuffled, and Johnny rolled over on the floor. "Mama! Mama!" he called.

"No fighting, boys!" Mama said cheerfully. "Johnny, you stay here with Mama. You help set the table for supper, eh? Let the others go out in the cold. We stay here warm, yes?"

When the other boys had thawed out a bit, they put on caps and mittens again and went out to feed Billy. They chopped wood, pumped buckets of water, and then locked up the barn and sheds. They worked fast and were soon back by the big kitchen stove again.

Mama chuckled when she saw their red noses. "Good hot soup with dumplings—that is what you need. Mama has a large pot full. As soon as Papa and the big boys come, we eat."

It was not long before Papa, Albert and Gus came into the warm kitchen. They were covered with snow.

Papa sniffed loudly. "I smelled Mama's soup down to the shop. So good it smelled, I could almost taste it."

"In this wind, Papa?" Charles asked, grinning.

"Of course, in this wind. It is blowing that way," Papa said.

Papa and the big boys took turns washing in the basin on the wooden bench in the kitchen. Before long they were ready to eat. Otto put

Henry in his high chair and they all gathered around the long table. Mama dished up a big tureen of steaming soup.

"Listen to the wind!" Albert said, his spoon halfway to his mouth. "You boys are going to be disappointed. No music lesson tonight, I bet. Mr. Walter won't try to make it in this storm."

"He will! He will!" Charles said angrily.

Albert chuckled. "Don't get mad at me, Charlie. It's not my fault."

Charles' glare melted and he smiled warmly at his big brother. "I know, Al. But I can't miss my lesson. It's the best part of the whole week!"

"Maybe Mr. Walter comes," Papa said soothingly. "We shall see. You make a good fire in the parlor stove, Otto, so we are ready, eh?"

After supper Papa took off his shoes and put on his carpet slippers. He sat down in his favorite rocker by the stove and took Johnny and

Henry on his knees. Charles brought a footstool and sat close by Papa's feet. Papa began to sing his favorite song:

"Oh, where, oh, where has my little dog gone?
  Oh, where, oh, where can he be?
    With his ears cut short and his tail cut long,
    Oh, where, oh, where is he?"

Otto made the fire in the parlor while Alf T. helped Mama do the dishes. Every few minutes the boys would look up at the big clock. It was getting later and later. Why didn't Mr. Walter come?

Papa rocked slowly back and forth. He was warm and contented. Henry dozed on Papa's lap. But Johnny was wide awake.

"Papa," Johnny said, reaching up to put chubby arms around his neck, "I want to take music lessons, too. I want to play a big horn like Mr. Walter's."

"I teach you to play the harmonica," Papa

said. He reached up onto a shelf and took down his battered old harmonica. He began to play a tune Johnny knew, and Johnny started to sing at the top of his voice:

"Hey, get along, get along, Josey;
   Hey, get along, Jim along, Joe!
Hey, get along, get along, Josey;
   Hey, get along, Jim along, Joe!"

Papa chuckled. "You sing, Johnny. You do not need to play the big horn."

"But all of us can sing," Johnny said. "I want to play a big horn."

Otto came out of the parlor and looked at the clock. "The fire is made, Papa. We are all ready for our lessons. Do you think he will come?"

Alf T. said softly, "It's going to be a dull evening. I had counted on my lesson."

Mama brought her knitting. She drew up her own rocking chair and settled herself comfortably in it. *"Ja,"* she agreed, "the music would make a happier evening. Why don't you boys practice a little? That would make music, no?"

Albert came to the parlor door. "Charles, Otto, Alf T., come in here a minute, will you, please?"

The boys went into the parlor and Albert shut the door tight behind them.

Mama smiled up at Papa. "We do not have much, Papa," she said, "but we manage to get instruments for our boys to play. And we give them lessons sometimes."

Papa nodded. "They get their love of music from you, Salome." He beamed. "You sing so well!"

"No, from you, Papa. You are the one with music in your heart."

Papa's round cheeks flushed happily. His brown eyes twinkled. But he only said, "It is good that our boys like music. It is very good."

2. *A Home Concert*

Albert opened the door from the parlor and looked into the kitchen. Henry was sound asleep, but Johnny was awake and wriggling.

"Johnny," Albert said softly, "come here."

Johnny slid to the floor and went into the parlor.

Albert shut the door behind him. "Listen, Johnny," he said. "We're going to surprise Mama and Papa with a little concert. The boys have all learned the same tune. They haven't had a chance to practice together. If they had tried to, of course Mama and Papa would have known, and it wouldn't be a surprise for them. Now, we want you to be in the concert, too."

"Yes," Johnny said, excited, "I want to—I want to. What can I play?"

"You have a very good ear for music, Johnny. Do you think you can listen closely and clap your hands in time with our playing?"

Johnny nodded.

"You must do it well, because this is a real concert. Stand over by Charles."

Charles had his trumpet in his hands. It was a battered old trumpet that Papa had bought for almost nothing, but Charles could make it sound as if it were brand-new. Alf T. had the horn that Mr. Walter had lent to him when he started taking lessons. Otto sat beside the bass drum he had been given on his twelfth birthday.

Albert went to the door and turned. "Remember, Johnny. Keep right in time with the boys. After the first piece, Charlie and Alf T. will play a duet. You can sit down while they're doing it."

Albert opened the door. "Mr. and Mrs. Ringling!" he called in a loud voice. "And young Mr. Augustus Ringling!"

Mama and Papa turned to look at Albert. Gus put down the piece of leather he was working on.

He was sitting back in a far corner of the room, his favorite spot, but he was not forgotten.

"Lady and Gentlemen," Albert went on, "you are invited to attend the first musical concert given by the famous Ringling brothers!"

Papa stood up with Henry in his arms. He shifted the baby to one arm and grandly offered the other to Mama. They pranced over to the parlor. Gus came along behind them, grinning a little at the foolishness.

The parlor was warm and cozy. The kerosene lamps on the table gave a soft glow. They showed Otto and Alf T., Charles and Johnny all waiting expectantly for Albert to give them the signal to begin.

"This way, please!" Albert said, and led his parents to the two matched parlor chairs. Gus sat down in a rocker. Albert turned and took a position in front of the four boys. He held

The trumpet and horn blared.

Mama's feather duster, with the handle pointing out, for his baton. He rapped the handle smartly against a chair back to attract the boys' eyes. Then he began to wave it.

The trumpet and horn blared. The drum's *rat-a-tat-tat* stressed the beat of the music.

"Come on, Johnny!" Albert whispered.

Johnny began to clap his hands softly in time to the music. They were playing "Old Folks at Home." When they came to "there's where the old folks stay," Otto's drum went *rub-a-dub-dub-rub-a-dub-dub* while Charles and Alf T. caught their breath.

After this selection, Papa and Mama and Gus clapped so loudly they wakened Henry, who clapped, too.

"Our second number will be a duet by Charles and Alf T. Ringling," Albert announced.

Alf T. went to the organ and Charles picked up his violin. He had taken more lessons on the violin than on the trumpet and dearly loved to play it. He plucked the strings as his brother played a few organ keys, to be sure they were in tune. Then they began. They played a song called "Down in the Valley."

Johnny had learned to sing this with Mama

Ringling. When the organ and violin began to wail, he could not keep still. He stood up and sang:

> "Down in the valley, valley so low,
>   Hang your head over, hear the wind blow!"

As the boys held that last note there came a loud, clear *"Baa-aa-aa!"*

The musicians and the audience looked at one another in surprise. They must be imagining things! Albert said, "Go on, boys." And they sang on:

> "Hear the wind blow, love,
>   Hear the wind blow——"

"Baaa-aa-aa! Baa-aa-aa!" Something hit the front door with a bang.

The music stopped. Gus ran to the door and opened it. In bounded Billy Rainbow, icicles hanging from his beard. He looked about at the gaping people, shook his head and gave another mournful bleat. The Ringlings rocked with laughter. Johnny and Charles ran and threw their arms about the shivering goat. They buried their faces in his neck, laughing and crying.

When Mama caught her breath she asked, "Didn't you lock the barn, Alf T.?"

"I thought I did, Mama. But the wind was blowing so hard. . . ." He began to giggle again.

"I'll take him back and see that he's tied in the warmest corner of the barn," Albert offered.

"Can't Billy stay in the house with us tonight, Mama?" Charles begged. "It's so cold out there!"

"I say not!" Mama answered firmly. "No goat in my home to sleep."

"You wanted to come in with the family, didn't you, Billy?" Charles said comfortingly to the bedraggled animal.

"He sang a goat song!" Johnny laughed.

While Albert got into his coat and overshoes, the brothers put away their instruments.

Papa stopped laughing long enough to say, "Thank you so much for the concert, boys!"

It was a struggle to get Billy out into the storm again, and Albert had his hands full. When the front door was shut behind them, Charles ran and threw himself against Papa's knees. "Oh, Papa," he said happily, "isn't Billy funny? If we ever have a real concert, do you think he will sing for us?"

Papa smiled down at him. "A real concert, you say, Charles? This tonight was a very real concert. But for the public, I think Billy should stay out of it, no?"

"But he was the best part." Charles giggled. "The very best part."

VI

A NEW HOME

1. *The First Break in the Family*

ONE afternoon Papa Ringling and Albert came home early from the harness shop. They were both excited.

"Well, Mama," Papa said happily, "well, boys, what do you say if we move across the river, eh?"

"Why, Papa, why?" the boys asked in chorus. "We like McGregor."

"Our friends are here," Charles added.

He was nine years old now, a tall, well-built youngster. His frank, friendly smile and his pleasant disposition made him a favorite wherever he went. He sang well, and could play almost any instrument he picked up.

"Yes, I know," Papa answered the boys, "but over in Wisconsin is fine opportunity for us. I have just heard about it. A new harness and carriage factory has been built. There are jobs for two good men—that means for Albert and me." He smiled. "William Traner, the owner, was at the shop today. He liked our work. He said if we come at once the jobs are ours."

"Regular pay every week," Albert added. "No worry! No taking stoves or carpets or groceries or music lessons in pay for our work. Always cash!"

Mama smiled encouragingly. She knew how hard it had been for Papa to make enough money to keep seven boys clothed and fed. And now that the boys were getting older, everything would cost more. A regular pay check would seem good.

"It will be nice, Papa." She beamed. "The boys will like it there. More people, new people, too, when they give a circus."

"And Prairie du Chien is growing fast," Papa

explained patiently. "When we came here to McGregor, this town, also, was a busy place. It was then a good place for a harness maker, with teamsters bringing in the farm stuff to be shipped downriver. But now—" he shrugged— "now that the railroad has come to Prairie du Chien, McGregor is losing much of its business. Luther Mason not only makes the harness, but also does the carriage repairs. His shop is enough for this town now. My business no longer is so good." He sighed.

The boys understood this. For months now, many of Papa's old customers had gone to Mason's bigger, newer shop. He had taken so much of the trade that even Gus had left Papa and gone to Mason's to work. "It is good," Papa had told Gus. "Luther and I are friends. He, too, must make a living." But it had been hard.

"Prairie du Chien," Charles said with disgust. "Prairie-dog town! And it lies so low and flat!"

He looked out the window at the tree-covered hills around McGregor. He knew he wouldn't like to live on level ground.

When Gus came home for supper and heard of the plan to move, he shook his head. "I'll stay here, Mama. I have a good job at Mason's. He was kind enough to give me work when Papa didn't have enough for both Albert and me."

Tears came to Mama's eyes. "You break the family up, August?" she asked gently. "How will we do when one of our boys is no longer under our roof?"

"I'll be only four miles away, Mama. I can come home often."

"August is right," Papa agreed. "He is a man, tall and strong. And his heart is in the harness business. There is no job waiting for him across the river, Mama."

Charles looked at Gus. Papa had said he was a man now. He was taller than Albert and heavier, too. And so different! Charles' eyes traveled to his oldest brother. Albert was his ideal of what a man should be. He was lithe and straight. He had practiced all sorts of stunts until now he could juggle four plates like the man in Dan Rice's show. He could walk a tightrope, and he could do tricks on the trapeze. In the barn loft he had rigged up trapeze bars, ladders, swinging rings. Here he practiced every night. And he let his younger brothers use them, too. But Gus never went to the loft. He was always busy making things of leather.

Charles' thoughts came around to his other brothers. How different from one another they were! Oh, they looked a good deal alike. Everyone said you could tell a Ringling a block away. And they all could sing, and all liked to perform. There was never an entertainment or a concert in McGregor that didn't include the Ringlings— all but Gus.

Yet they were different. Otto always had money. At fourteen he was still the brother who always had money. And he was usually willing to help the others when they needed it. Alf T. still was the quiet, gentle-voiced one. And Johnny still was the clown. And, Charles added to himself, glancing at the baby, Henry imitated Johnny in everything he did.

"It is good that we go now," Mama pointed out. "Johnny is six. He must go to school. We must get settled so he will be ready to start school right away."

"Will we take all our things?" Charles asked. "Billy Rainbow?"

"*Ja! Ja!*" Mama nodded vigorously. "We leave behind only our Augustus!"

2. *Good-by! Good-by, McGregor!*

It was a bright autumn morning when the Ringlings said good-by to McGregor, where

they had lived for twelve years. Here the four
younger boys had been born. It was the only
town they knew and they already felt homesick
for it.

Papa borrowed a wagon from his next-door
neighbor, Mr. Koss. It was big enough to hold
everything the family owned. Aaron and Anna
Koss stood and watched sadly as all the house-
hold goods were carried out and stored inside.
They hated to see their playmates go.

When the wagon was packed, Papa helped
Mama up onto the high wagon seat. He lifted
four-year-old Henry to sit beside her. Charles
and Johnny were already sitting in their bright
red wagon with Billy Rainbow hitched to it.
They, too, would ride the mile to the dock, but the
other boys would walk.

"You'd better get going, Charlie!" Albert said.

Charles gave Billy a smart flick with the whip.

The little procession set out with the older boys walking behind the small wagon.

"Tell your papa that Gus will bring the wagon back tonight, Aaron," Papa Ringling called.

"All right, Mr. Ringling. Good-by! Good-by, Charlie!" Aaron waved his hand.

"Good-by, Johnny!" Anna shouted. "Come back often."

"Good-by! Good-by!" the boys answered.

The little procession moved down the steep street toward the river. Friends and neighbors came to their gates to wave farewell. Chad and Mike Hood ran along beside Otto and Alf T.

"This is just like a parade," Johnny said, his eyes shining.

"Something like," Charles agreed, "but unlike, too. When we had that parade last summer, we knew we'd see all the people again tomorrow."

"We'll miss our old friends, but we'll see new

The little procession moved down the street.

faces," Alf T. said softly, walking close to the little wagon.

"There she is!" Charles exclaimed as he caught sight of the dock. "There's the *Lady*

Franklin! I've always wanted to take a ride on her."

The little ferryboat was familiar to everyone in McGregor and Prairie du Chien. It made the trip daily between the two towns.

At the sight of the small boat, with its curious hull curved up at each end like a sled, the boys quickened their steps. They forgot the sadness of leaving friends and playmates and thought only of the fun of a boat ride on the river.

"How long will it take, Al?" Charles called.

"Not long. Prairie du Chien is only a couple of miles up the river——"

"And on the other side," Gus put in. "That adds another mile and a half."

They reached the dock and Charles carefully drove Billy up the wide gangplank and onto the deck. Gus fastened the goat securely to the rail. A moment later Papa drove the loaded wagon onto the boat.

Charles and Johnny climbed out and ran to the boat rail. They looked up at the town they were leaving, high on the bank above them.

"Good-by, McGregor!" they shouted.

Albert turned and looked up the river. "Hello, Prairie du Chien!" he said cheerfully. "Here come the Ringlings!"

3. *Old Junk and the Circus Box*

"I like school, Mama!" Johnny said as he and Charles came into the kitchen of their new home in Prairie du Chien.

Mama smiled and ran her fingers through Johnny's thick, curly hair. "I thought so, my Johnny. You already have found new playmates, eh?"

"Yes, Mama, lots of playmates. And we're going to have a program at school. I'm going to sing."

"A program already?" Mama looked surprised. "It is only the first week of school yet."

"Yes, but, Mama," Charles explained, "over here we have a program every Friday afternoon. Teacher said I could play my violin."

"It is good, then, that you boys have had music lessons. Now you can do something nice on the programs. What are you going to sing, Johnny?"

Johnny didn't have to be asked twice. He laid down his slate, stood up in front of Mama and began to sing:

> "Joseph Baxter is my name
> (My friends call me Joe).
> I'm wise, you know, to every game;
> Every trick I know.
> I once was green as green could be
> (I suffered for it, though).
> Now if they try their games on me,
> I tell them, 'Not for Joe!'"

> "Not for Joe! Not for Joe!
> No! No! No! Not for Joe!
> Not for Joseph! Oh, dear no!"

He finished with a little jig step, bowed, and waited for his mother to clap.

Charles grinned. "Johnny always expects applause. And he always gets it."

"Naturally," Mama agreed. "You get what you expect to get—if you work for it. And Johnny works for his applause. He learns the new songs and he sings them well."

Charles glanced at the clock on the shelf by the stove. "We ought to get out and look for junk," he said. "Come on, Johnny!"

"I want you to play with Henry," Mama said with a smile. "He gets lonely now Johnny is in school. Now he is home alone all day."

"He can come with us, Mama," Charles said.

"What do you mean—look for junk? Never in McGregor did you look for junk."

"We didn't know about it over there. Jimmy Clayton told us about it. Over by the river there's a man—Junkman Joe. He'll buy empty bottles, old horseshoes, scrap iron—anything. Now that Otto and Alf T. have jobs after school, they can put money in our circus box. Johnny and I have to do something so we can, too."

"Yes, Otto and Alf T., they run errands and deliver small packages for the store. That is good, respectable work. But junk!" Mama's nose wrinkled in dislike.

"All we do, Mama, is walk around and pick up empty bottles. That's respectable, isn't it?" Charles pleaded.

Mama sighed. "That circus box! Do you think you boys can save enough money to buy a tent, eh?"

"We're trying to. Over here, in this bigger town, we have to give a better circus than we ever did in McGregor, or they'll think we're rubes! Country Jakes! Know-nothings!" Charles wrinkled his nose to show how others would look at them in scorn. "By next summer we ought to have enough to buy a tent—or the stuff to make one."

"The circuses we gave in McGregor were dandy!" Johnny protested. "People paid a penny a ticket at the last one, didn't they?"

"Yes," Charles admitted, "they did, but everyone over there knew us. Here it's different."

Just then a voice outside called, "Charlie! Charlie Ringling!"

"That's Jimmy, Mama, my new friend. Please let me go with him?"

"If you take Henry. And be careful, boys. I guess maybe it is all right today. After this I ask Papa what he thinks."

"Come along, Henry," Charles said, taking his little brother's hand. He didn't need to say "Come along" to Johnny. The three went off.

Mama Ringling sighed. "New things they learn every day. But they are good boys. I think maybe junk is all right."

VII

THE MENAGERIE GROWS

1. *A Real Bargain*

O<small>N</small> Saturday afternoon Charles and Johnny went to the junkman's.

"Here, Mr. Joe, is the junk we picked up this week." Charles shifted the gunny sack from his shoulder and started to empty it.

"Never mind, Charlie," the old man said. "I'm quitting business. I have quit, in fact. Now I'm selling instead of buying."

"Selling!" Charles exclaimed. "Then what do we do with this stuff?"

Joe shrugged. "The fellow that's bought my place may do business with you."

Charles began to pick up the horseshoes and old iron he had dumped out.

"You fellows don't happen to know anyone who'd buy Champ?" Joe asked.

Charles and Johnny turned to look at the junkman's horse. He was a sorry-looking animal—nothing but skin and bones.

"Are you going to sell Champ?" Johnny asked.

"Got to. I'm going down river."

"How much are you asking for him?" Charles said slowly.

"Well, fellows, I won't fib to you. I'm not really asking anything. If I could just get a good home for him, and maybe a dollar or two—— But do you know I can't get even that? I can't even give him away."

Charles looked at Johnny and Johnny looked at Charles. Then they both looked at Joe.

"Maybe we know someone who'd take him," Charles said.

"Well, of course, now, you recall I said I

wanted a dollar or two. I ought to have something!" Joe said quickly.

"We'll see about it." Charles hoisted his sack of junk. "Come on, Johnny. We'll let you know tomorrow."

When they were out of earshot, Charles said "I'd buy him. But I don't know what Otto will think, and he handles the circus-box money."

"Why?" Johnny demanded. "Why is Otto always the boss who tells us what to do with the money? We all put some in the box."

"He's the oldest of us four, and the savingest," Charles explained. "And we agreed to let him have the say-so, unless we outvoted him."

Indeed, when Charles and Johnny told their brothers about the chance to buy a horse for almost nothing, Alf T. was eager. "He said only a dollar or two, Otto," he urged. "We can take that out of the circus box."

Otto was wary. "If we take money out of the

circus box, we'll never save enough to buy a tent."

"But we need a horse for our circus," Charles cried. "It's the best thing we could have!"

"Well, we can't do anything tomorrow. It's Sunday. But we'll go down Monday before school and look at this Champ," Otto promised at last.

"He'll be sold by then," Charles said desperately.

But Champ wasn't sold. Joe came out of his shack when he saw the four boys looking the horse over carefully. "He's a mighty smart animal," the junkman observed. "Knows more than you'd think."

Otto shook his head. "A horse is no good to us without a wagon," he said thoughtfully. "And Champ here doesn't look as if he's much good to anyone. Now—" Otto nodded toward a rickety old wagon that stood in Joe's cluttered yard—

"if you could throw that wagon in, we might think about it."

Joe hunkered down, picked up a straw and chewed on it. He considered the matter. At last he said, "Three dollars?"

The three younger boys' eyes were begging Otto to say yes. But Otto shook his head. "You told my brothers two dollars."

"That was just for Champ," Joe pointed out.

"We'd just buy Champ. You'd have to throw the wagon in to get us to buy the horse."

Joe grinned suddenly. "You're a businessman all right, young fellow. You've got a good head on your shoulders. It's a bargain. You give me two dollars and take the horse and wagon."

"And that old harness?" Otto persisted. "It's no good without a horse or wagon."

"Sure. Take the whole lot!"

Otto brought his hand out of his pocket. It was filled with pennies and nickels and dimes. He

carefully counted out two dollars and held it out
to Joe.

The others watched until the money had
changed hands. Then they rushed with a yell
toward Champ. The animal was too low-spirited
to notice what was happening. He stood patiently while Otto and Alf T. got the makeshift
harness on him. Then Otto led him over to the
light, high-wheeled wagon and backed him up
between the shafts.

Alf T. fastened buckles while Otto walked
around the wagon, examining it. Charles and
Johnny climbed into the front seat, chattering
excitedly.

"I think it will hold up till we get home," Otto
decided at last. "Here, you two, get in the back
seat. Alf T. and I will have to drive until we
know whether the horse is really tame."

Alf T. chuckled and winked at Otto. "He's
tame, right enough. But wait till we've had him

awhile. Remember how Billy Rainbow looked when we got him?"

Laughing, Otto took the lines. He snapped them against Champ's back, but the horse made no move. He tried again and again, but without the slightest response.

"You drive, Alf T. I'll get down and lead him."

So, with Otto holding the bridle close to Champ's mouth and almost dragging him along, they managed to get their purchase home.

When the little procession came into the yard, Mama Ringling shook her head in utter dismay. But there was no time to argue with the boys now, no time even for them to unharness Champ. They had to run fast to get to school before the bell rang.

"Will you do it this once, Mama, please?" Otto begged. "He can't stand in the harness all day."

"I should say not!" Mama agreed. "He would fall down dead before noon."

So, with the delighted Henry helping her, Mama unharnessed Champ and gave him some grain and water. As she fed him, her heart was touched by the animal's sad eyes and gaunt body.

"You have not been treated good!" she grumbled angrily. "It is a pity anyone lets a creature get so thin!"

She patted Champ's nose and the horse looked at her gratefully. By the time the boys came home that afternoon, Mama's heart had been won by the sad-faced animal.

2. *Charles Makes a Deal*

At school Charles bragged about Champ. They had owned the horse only a week, but already he was perking up and looking lively. "My big brother, Albert, is making a harness for him—a real harness. And we're going to paint the wagon red. And next summer we're going to have a circus."

"How can you have a circus?" Jimmy Clayton wanted to know. "I saw a circus in St. Paul last summer. There was a big tent, and there were acrobats and clowns and wild animals and——"

"I know," Charles said. "We've seen real circuses, too. Over in McGregor we had one every summer almost."

"I'm going to be in the circus," Johnny put in. "I'm the clown!"

"Can I be in it, too?" Jimmy asked.

"Can you do any tricks?" Charles wanted to know.

Jimmy shook his head sadly. "No, I can't. But I'm trying to teach my pet badger some. Only he's so dumb he won't learn!"

Charles' eyes widened. "Have you got a pet badger, really?"

Jimmy nodded. "Maybe by next summer I can teach him some tricks."

Charles said eagerly, "Look, Jimmy. I'll make a deal with you. You can be in our circus, if you'll lend us your badger. Let Alf T. and me train him. We trained Billy Rainbow and we're going to train Champ. You bring him over to our barn and let *us* train him. Then we'll let *you* be in our circus."

Jimmy thought there might be something in this. After he had left them, Johnny said to Charles, "Maybe Otto won't let you keep your promise to Jimmy."

"Why not?" Charles demanded. "It won't take any money out of the circus box. And we'll have another animal for our menagerie." But he was just a bit doubtful all the same.

"We really have a menagerie!" Otto chuckled.

That very afternoon, after school, Jimmy brought his badger over to the Ringlings' barn and left him for Charles and Alf T. to train. "But he's still *my* badger," Jimmy insisted.

Otto was so amused at the badger's funny ways that he agreed to the deal Charles had made with his friend.

The week before, Otto and Alf T. had caught a squirrel. They had built a cage with a wheel in it. The squirrel, too, was in the barn with the badger and Champ and Billy Rainbow.

"We really have a menagerie—of sorts!" Otto chuckled, standing in the barn and looking about proudly. "We can have a Prairie du Chien circus next summer that will be well worth a nickel a ticket."

"A nickel!" Charles exclaimed. "We'll get rich!"

"If enough people come," Alf T. said.

"Well," Otto said, "that's your department, Alf T. You make up some good dodgers. Maybe you can get a story in the paper here. We'll fill our tent chuck-full."

Alf T. nodded. Yes, this was his department. No one disputed that he could handle words better than any of the others. His dodgers at McGregor had brought in the crowd.

"We can have a parade," Charles said eagerly, "a humdinger of a parade. Oh, how I wish the winter was over and school was out!"

VIII

THE TOWN TAKES NOTICE

1. *A Tent Like Joseph's Coat*

SUMMER came at last. School closed, and the Ringling boys turned their full attention to the circus they had been working on all winter. They had worked on it whenever they could find the time. They had practiced tumbling stunts. They had learned new pieces to play and new songs to sing.

Albert had been their instructor. He had practiced with them, and had helped them a great deal. He was as interested in the circus as the younger boys.

They had done more than practice. They had painted barrel hoops for Albert to juggle. They had made tights of their old winter underwear.

They had dyed them bright blue and red and green. They had made "plumes" of dyed sheep's wool. They had fashioned pompons of colored paper cut into thin strips and curled by pulling them over the blade of a kitchen knife. They had made stovepipe hats of cardboard blackened with stove polish.

The boys had found an abandoned icehouse down by the river. In past winters, great blocks of ice had been cut from the frozen Mississippi and stored there. Buried deep in sawdust, the ice would not melt all summer long. But as Prairie du Chien had grown, a fine, new icehouse had been built, and the old one was left to fall into ruin. The sawdust, however, had not been removed, and the boys, with a great deal of effort, carried it to the yard to make a real sawdust ring in their tent.

They covered the sawdust pile with old boards and blankets until they could get a tent. The tent was the great problem. The younger boys had found no solution.

The first day of vacation they gathered around the kitchen table. Otto emptied the circus box and stared down, frowning at the little pile of coins.

"We can never get a tent with that!" he said bitterly. "I told you and told you, that if we kept dipping into the box we'd not have enough!"

"But we needed paint and dye and paper and things," Charles pointed out. "We couldn't have a circus without them."

"And we sure can't have a circus without a tent!" Otto scooped up the coins and thrust them back into the box.

"We can't back out!" Charles cried. "We've told everybody we're going to have a circus."

"Well, we'll just have to wait." Otto put the box back on the shelf and stalked away. He was now a big boy of fifteen, but he looked almost as if he wanted to get away and have a good cry by himself.

When Albert came home that night, Charles brought up their big trouble. "What can we do, Al? Otto's mad and Alf T. feels bad. None of us knows what to do. And we've bragged to everybody about our circus!"

Albert considered the problem. Suddenly he smiled. "Tell you what, Charlie: we'll *make* a tent. I think we can make a fine tent, though it won't be fully a canvas-top. You boys hunt around and collect everything that might possibly be used."

"But what—?" Charles began.

"Start with that old canvas wagon top we've been using to practice tumbling on. Clean it up. Patch the holes. Then add anything, anything at all that can possibly be used. Put that good brain of yours to work, Charlie. You'll find things."

Charlie grinned up at his brother. "I knew you'd think of something, Al."

They all went right to work, and two nights later they showed Albert what they had collected. There was the old wagon top, scrubbed clean, a worn oilcloth table cloth Mama had thrown away, and a roll of rag carpet they had brought from McGregor. They hadn't had to use this in the house, because here they had store carpet on the parlor floor. There was a heap of gunny sacks, canvas grain bags, ragged quilts and blankets.

Albert chuckled as he looked over the pile. "All right, boys. You've done a good job. We can use the patched-up canvas wagon top for the tent top. The tent must be at least nine feet high, so cut and sew together everything you have here into a long strip, nine feet wide, for the tent walls."

"That will be quite a job!" Otto remarked,

frowning as he thought of the sore fingers they all would have.

"But you boys can do it, Otto. And look at the money you'll save! Now," he went on, "I sent a note to Gus and he'll come home on his Saturday half holiday. Then we'll get the tent poles and help you rig up the tent for the Ringling Brothers' Circus!"

"Gus! Gus! He's going to aid! Now the circus is surely made!" Johnny chanted.

"He said he'd help if we didn't ask him to get out in front of people and make a donkey of himself."

They roared at this. It was so like Gus.

"It's too bad to leave the baby out," Alf T. said.

"But she's not one of the Ringling brothers," Johnny joked.

The other boys smiled at this. During the winter a little sister, the first Ringling girl, had been born. She had been named Ida. The boys agreed she was the most wonderful thing ever. But they couldn't think of any way to use a tiny baby girl in their circus. And Mama wouldn't hear of it anyway!

They set to work. They patched the canvas wagon top with the red oilcloth table cover. They measured and cut and sewed. Out on the lawn the strip of odds and ends grew longer and longer. When Mama saw how hard the boys kept at it, she said, "The baby is sleeping now. Would you like Mama's good needle to help a little?"

Charles flung his arms about her. "Oh, Mama, thank you! Maybe now we can get it done by Saturday."

When Albert came home on Saturday the younger brothers showed what they had accomplished. Gus was there, too.

"The top's done, but I'm afraid there's not enough for the sides after all," Alf T. said.

The big boys measured the strip for the wall

and shook their heads, feeling sorry for their younger brothers.

"Could we use the barn for one side of the tent?" Charles asked. "Then we'd have enough, wouldn't we? And we could use the barn for a dressing room and come into the tent through this side door."

Albert chuckled. "Idea-man Charles! That's a great plan. Now, right after dinner, Gus and I'll go find a center pole."

The two big boys—men they were now at nineteen and twenty-one—went down to a grove near the river. They found a strong straight tree about fifteen feet tall and not too large around. They cut it down and stripped off the limbs. Then they carried the pole home.

Next, they dug a hole in the backyard, just the right distance from the barn. Into this hole they put one end of the tree trunk and anchored it firmly with side supports. This would be the center pole of the tent.

The Ringlings owned a stepladder, and they borrowed another from a neighbor. They put one against the center pole and the other close beside it.

Al and Gus started to pull one end of the heavy canvas top over them. Its sides of carpet and blankets made the tent heavy. Slowly they climbed the ladders, dragging the tent along with them. Suddenly there was trouble.

"Help!" Albert shouted as the canvas slipped from his hands. Its pull was too hard. Al fell, and that made Gus topple off too. They were buried under its smothering folds.

Otto, Alf T., Charles, Johnny and even little Henry ran to the rescue. They tugged and pulled, and got the canvas off their brothers. Al and Gus got up, brushed themselves off, and shook their heads. But they weren't a bit hurt.

Papa saw the trouble and came out.

"My! My!" he said, chuckling. "You need an expert roustabout, eh? I will help. Fasten one side to the barn first, then it will be easier, no?"

With Papa's assistance and the boys lending a hand, the tent top was finally stretched out over the center pole. Its sides were staked down. The tent was up!

The boys stood back to examine it. Mama came out with Baby Ida in her arms.

"My, my, what a pretty tent!" Mama said. "It is just as pretty as Joseph's coat of many colors."

The boys looked at one another and burst into a laugh. They knew the Bible story—how Jacob had made his favorite son a coat of many colors.

"That's it! That's it!" Alf said excitedly. "I can use that on my dodgers. It ought to bring the people in."

"And when, then, is this fine circus to be?" Papa asked.

"Next Saturday, Papa, if Mr. Traner will let you and Al have the whole day off," Charles said.

Papa nodded. "He's a good man. I think he will contribute that much to the famous Ringling brothers." He chuckled.

2. *"Hold Your Horses!"*

On the morning of the circus, Charles was the first one awake. He thumped Johnny, who slept with him. "Wake up! Wake up! The sun's shining. It's a fine day for the circus."

The noise awakened the other boys in their beds in the big upstairs room. Heads popped up. Eyes blinked. Then each one was out of bed in one jump. Jeans and shirts were pulled on in a jiffy, and they were ready for the great day.

Charles ran to the window and looked down at their tent. It didn't look too strange, after all. And inside it was like a real circus tent. With the coins that the circus box held they had bought strips of red calico to make a ring inside of which the performers would present their acts.

"I just hope it doesn't rain," Charles muttered, worried. "Those patches on the top might not hold."

"It won't rain! It won't rain!" chanted Johnny. "Not a drop to spoil our top!"

When they came downstairs, Mama had breakfast ready.

"Sit down and eat a good breakfast, boys," Albert advised. "Circus people take time to eat hearty."

"We're glad you and Papa got the whole day off, Al. That was nice of Mr. Traner. Your juggling tricks are worth the whole price of the show."

Albert grinned. "None of your blarney, Otto. In this circus everyone is a star performer."

"Even me!" little Johnny sang out.

In spite of Albert's suggestion that they eat a good breakfast, they hurried through the meal. Then they dashed upstairs to dress for the parade.

Charles was the first one dressed. "How do I look?" he asked.

Otto glanced up from fastening the belt of his doublet. "You're all right. But help Johnny. He's put his doublet on backward."

Alf T. was dressing Henry. "I want tights like Johnny's," Henry complained. "I want red tights."

"We haven't any more and yours are really prettier, Henry," Alf T. soothed the little boy.

"His green tights aren't very pretty are they?" Johnny whispered to Charles.

"The knit underwear didn't take the green dye so well," Charles explained. "But he looks fine, anyway. . . . Your tights fit best of all, Johnny," Charles added, with a smile.

Charles looked down at his own legs. The knit

underwear was a bit wrinkled and baggy on him. The doublets looked well on all the boys, because Mama had cut down gunny sacks to just the proper size for each. They fitted closely, covering them from shoulder to thigh. Albert had decided that as a professional juggler, he would need a dress coat for his costume. He had made one by cutting away the front of a coat Papa had outworn. Then he had shaped the back part into "tails." A stovepipe hat and stiff white cardboard collar completed his elegant outfit.

In return for the use of the badger, the boys had given Jimmy Clayton the honor of marching at the head of the parade to announce its coming. Mama had made him a fine suit from an old sheet, dyed bright red. The boys were barely dressed when Jimmy arrived, as excited as his friends. This was the very first time he had ever had a part in a show of any kind. Two of Charles' friends had been invited to bring their new express wagon to carry a box holding two garter snakes.

While Charles and Johnny hitched Billy Rainbow to the little express wagon, Alf T. and Otto harnessed Champ to the two-seated wagon.

"Joe wouldn't recognize Champ now," Alf T. said proudly. "Look at him, so sleek and fat."

"He wouldn't recognize his old wagon either. All the loose parts are nailed up, and the whole thing has been painted yellow and——" Otto began.

"All but the wheels and the seats," Charles corrected. The wheels were a bright red, the seats blue. On one side Alf T. had painted "Ringlings' Great Circus."

The procession formed in the yard. First came Billy Rainbow, his long hair brushed and his horns painted gold. Charles grinned when he remembered what a struggle he had had to get Otto to let him buy enough gold paint for those horns. Billy's hoofs were now painted bright red, and he had strips of red calico braided into his forelock. He pulled the express wagon, with Johnny and Henry sitting proudly on the high seat. Johnny was driving. In the wagon was one cage holding the pet squirrel, and another in which their orange-striped cat prowled back and forth, lashing its tail.

Mama was watching the boys. She turned to Albert. "Is it safe for Johnny to drive Billy?"

"Yes, Mama. He's a good driver. And Billy is so fat and lazy now, there's no danger."

Next came Charles' friend, Luther Green, pulling his little wagon with the box of snakes. Then Luther's brother, Kurt, followed, leading the badger on a stout cord.

Last of all marched Champ, with red ribbons braided in mane and tail. Curled paper plumes nodded on his bridle. He drew the band wagon, with Albert in his dress suit as driver. Charles and Alf T. and Otto formed the band. Otto had his drum, Alf T. his trombone and Charles his horn.

Out of the yard moved the procession. Jimmy Clayton marched ahead and shouted, "Hold your horses! Here comes the parade!"

The band struck up one of the tunes practiced for this occasion, "Oh, Susannah." After that it played "Remember the Alamo!" and "Seeing the Elephant."

People came to their doors to watch. Shopkeepers and customers hurried out to the sidewalk. Children ran along beside the little wagons, shouting and yelling. When Jimmy's badger turned on them, they didn't know whether they should be frightened.

From his seat on the wagon, Albert tossed out handbills the boys had made. These said: "The

Mothers and fathers came,

big circus will begin at two o'clock in the Ringlings' yard. Price: children 5¢, adults 10¢."

3. *Every Trick They Knew*

Otto had the job of selling the tickets. The
band wagon was now the ticket wagon. Otto

leading tiny boys and girl.

stood in it with a box in front of him. The tickets were made from old pasteboard shoe boxes the boys had begged from a storekeeper.

Albert was the barker. Dressed in his black suit and tall hat, he stood at the front gate, shouting, "Ladies and gentlemen! Come one! Come all! Only a dime, one thin dime, to see the great

Ringlings' Circus. Children a nickel—half a dime."

Children came running down the street. There had not been a circus in Prairie du Chien this summer. They were eager to see this one. Some mothers and fathers came, leading tiny boys and girls.

The older people giggled at the sight of the makeshift tent. But when they got inside they decided it was going to be a real circus, after all. Around the sawdust ring, the children sat on benches made by putting planks across empty wooden boxes and barrels. There were chairs for the grownups.

Alf T. took the tickets at the tent entrance. He was watching the tent fill up. There might not be seats for everyone. Then he remembered Dan Rice and how he had put the overflow crowd "on the straw." It'll be "on the grass" for us, he told himself.

At last he ran out to speak to Albert. "You'd better stop, Al. The tent's plumb full."

Albert nodded. "Come on, Otto. Close down the ticket window. It's time to start anyway. We don't want our audience to grow restless and raise a clem, like the one you had at your panorama show."

Otto jumped down from the ticket wagon and all three hurried around to slip into the barn. There Charles, Johnny and Henry, Jimmy Clayton and the two Green boys were chattering excitedly. Albert made his way to the cracked mirror they had propped up on a box. He dusted off his coat and trousers and straightened his tie. He put his tall hat on at a jaunty angle and looked at himself in the glass. Then he went to the barn door, passed through it, and stepped before the filled tent.

"Ladies and gentlemen!" he began in his best showman's voice, "your attention, please! You are now about to witness the one and only, the magnificent Ringling Brothers' Circus, brought to you from McGregor, Iowa!"

At this, some of the larger boys began to shout "Boo!" and Albert saw at once that it had been a mistake to mention the smaller town. So he added with a wink, "where it played a one-night stand!" The boys laughed at this and the older people clapped in appreciation of Albert's quick wit. "Now, first of all, the grand entrance!"

In the barn Otto heard the words "grand entrance." They were the cue for him as leader of the performers. He gave a signal and the band marched in, playing a lively air. Behind them came the "guest performers" and Henry leading the animals. Billy Rainbow, driven by Johnny, brought up the rear.

They all marched once around the ring, out the door and back into the barn to await their turns to perform.

Alf T. grabbed Charles' arm. "Did you see him?" he whispered. "A man from the newspaper! I went into the office and talked to them about our circus. Now they've sent a man to see it."

Charles' eyes were wide. "We'll have to do our best. Do you think, Alf—?" He couldn't put it into words. What if they were written up in the paper!

Charles joined the others to peek through the door and watch what went on. Albert was in the center of the ring, juggling. He was whirling china plates on his two forefingers.

Charles leaned close to Johnny. "See that! Al used to break Mama's plates." Then he thought of the paper again. Would it make fun of their show?

A little later Jimmy Clayton nudged him. "I've never seen Al do that trick."

Now Albert was lying on his back. He was

whirling a keg on his uplifted feet by moving them as if he were running. At the same time he held his arms up and twirled the plates.

"Wait till you see him do his brand-new buggy-whip balancing. He's been practicing every noon down at the harness shop. It's his own original trick."

"He's starting it now." Jimmy pushed Charles a little to one side so he might get a better look. Albert was balancing a buggy whip on his chin while still twirling the keg and the plates.

The audience was watching with mouths open, eyes wide. Now Albert gave the keg one last bounce and sent it rolling across the sawdust. He leaped to his feet, catching the plates in one hand, the whip in the other. He bowed, smiling, to right and left. The children clapped and stamped and shouted. Albert ran out of the tent, into the barn.

Albert was in the center of the ring, juggling.

Now Otto, Alf T. and Charles marched in.
Each one carried two musical instruments. Otto
had a drum and a concertina; Alf T., his trombone and harmonica; Charles, his horn and a
triangle. They began to play "Yankee Doodle,"

and as they played, each boy switched back and forth from one instrument to the other. They didn't make the change all together, but hit-and-miss, so the watching children were kept guessing which three instruments would be playing at any one moment. The three-boy band was a clever stunt and they had worked hard to get it right. The audience showed their appreciation by loud applause.

"Go back in," Albert whispered when they came from the tent. "You'll have to give them an encore."

"We can't play any other tune this way," Otto objected.

"Then play 'Yankee Doodle' again. But look! Take Johnny in with you this time, and let him sing."

The three grabbed Johnny and ran back into the tent, and the people stopped clapping. The music began, this time with Johnny singing, too:

> "Yankee Doodle came to town,
>   Riding on a pony.
> He stuck a feather in his cap
>   And called it macaroni!"

This time the applause was even louder than before. Back in the barn, Albert said, "That's enough of 'Yankee Doodle.' It's time for the acrobats."

Charles, Johnny and Henry ran into the ring. They turned handsprings and somersaults. Then Jimmy came running out and they built a pyramid. Johnny sat on the shoulders of the two larger boys, as they crouched close together. Henry stood up on Johnny's shoulders. They posed for a moment. Then Charles and Jimmy jumped away. But instead of falling, Johnny and Henry jumped, too. All turned cartwheels and came up together. They ran out amid clapping.

"Animal stunts!" Otto called.

Charles led in the badger. Even Albert had not been able to teach this animal any tricks. But Charles led him slowly around the ring, and by pulling on the leash just right he made the badger turn this way and that. The little boys leaned forward to see the beady little eyes and sharp teeth. The little girls screeched.

Then Johnny led in the orange cat, who stood on its hind legs and boxed with him.

Alf T. brought in the squirrel cage. While he played the harmonica, the squirrel sent its wheel flying around and around.

"Now, Johnny, it's your turn with Billy," Otto said. "This is our best act, so do it right." He started a *rat-a-tat-tat* on his drum.

Alf T. walked into the ring leading Billy, with Johnny on Billy's back, clinging tightly to the long hair. Around the ring they ran twice, while the drum kept up its thrilling tattoo. Then Alf T. led Billy to the center of the ring, and Charles marched in carrying a painted barrel. He set it on end in the center of the ring. The crowd grew silent, wondering what would happen next.

"Up!" Alf T. ordered, snapping his fingers.

Billy recognized the order. He gave a quick bound onto the barrel. Johnny was supposed to cling on, but he was thrown backward with such a jerk that his fingers let go of the long hair. He landed on his back, feet in the air. Billy stood proudly, his four hoofs close together on the barrel head.

The crowd yelled in delight and amusement. Charles bent over Johnny. "Are you hurt?" he whispered.

Johnny didn't bother to answer. He turned a backward somersault and came to his feet, smiling and bowing. Otto's drum went *rat-a-tat-tat*. Albert dashed out and got the horn in the barn and blew a clear, sharp *tantara*. All the other performers ran into the tent to stand around Billy and bow.

The children streamed out of the tent. "It was a good circus!" they shouted. "Have another one. We'll come."

"That Johnny's a real showman," Albert said, "the way he turned his fall into a trick."

4. *Newspaper Publicity*

That evening Papa looked up from the Prairie du Chien *Weekly*. "Did you see this, Mama?" he asked, beaming. "Our boys, they are in the newspaper already."

"Are we, Papa? Let's see!" The boys crowded around. "Read it aloud, Papa. Read it!" they begged.

Papa read: " 'This morning the people of

Prairie du Chien were treated to a rare spectacle —a circus parade got up entirely by the Ringling boys and their neighbors.'" He paused, his eyes going down the story. "It says it was 'a magnificent and amazing boys' parade, with plumes of sheep's wool dyed red and blue, pompons of curled colored paper and a surprising menagerie.' What do you think of that? And look! Here it tells about the circus, too."

"Read it. Read it!"

"'The circus performance revealed a great deal of originality and showmanship. Each boy had his own part to do and did it without a single hitch. The juggling by Albert Ringling was the best we've ever seen. As a climax what seemed an accident was turned into a clever stunt by little Johnny Ringling.'"

"See, Mama?" Papa beamed. "The Ringling boys are famous, no?"

Albert turned to Alf T. "You're the one to thank for this, Alf T.," he said. "You're smart, getting the paper to pay attention to us."

"That's worth real money," Otto added. "It's better than a paid-for advertisement."

IX

THE BROTHERS ORGANIZE

1. *The First Step*

IT was a lovely June evening in 1882. Baraboo, Wisconsin, lay bathed in the rosy colors of sunset. Its tree-shaded streets seemed to say that here everyone was peaceful and happy. But nineteen-year-old Charles Ringling was not happy. His frown seemed out of place on that pleasant evening. And his unhappy expression was very much out of place on his handsome face.

He turned toward Johnny, who was walking along beside him. "We're wasting our lives away," he grumbled. "We don't have enough work to keep us busy. The odd jobs we get now and then aren't worth much." He kicked at the dust of the sidewalk like a cross little boy.

"I know," Johnny agreed, "but what can we

do? Papa has tried other towns—Milwaukee, Stillwater. There just isn't any work anywhere. He thought we'd do well here at Baraboo when he came to work for Uncle Henry Moeller. But you know Papa. He's not happy working for anyone else. That's why he opened his own shop again."

"And it burned down!" Charles said bitterly. After a pause he went on, "Papa took prizes at the fair last year and he has enough work to keep his own hands busy. It's just that there are so many of us and we eat so much. Even with Al and Gus and Otto gone away to work, we're too many for Papa. What little we can earn around here in hard times doesn't help much."

They were coming home from a day's work for a merchant in the village. It wasn't often they could get a full day's work. Both boys hated odd jobs, but they didn't let their parents know it. So as they reached Papa's harness shop, they wiped the frowns from their faces and began to smile. Then they went bounding up the stairs to the apartment over the shop. Mama would have supper ready.

They burst open the door and stopped in their tracks. Charles rushed forward. "Al! Al!" he shouted. "When did you arrive?"

He gave Al a big bear hug, and then turned to Al's wife. "Louise! This is wonderful! Have you come for a visit?"

At that moment Charles caught sight of Otto and rushed to him. "Say, what is this? A family reunion or something?"

Johnny was greeting the newcomers, too. In the excitement of the moment neither Charles nor Johnny noticed that Mama's eyes were bright with tears. She came bustling over as the questions tumbled from Charles' lips. "Now, now,

Charlie! You go get ready for supper. After we eat, then we talk, no?"

"But Mama——"

"No 'but Mama' now. Wash up good and quick. The supper is ready and waiting. Later, we ask questions."

"What's the idea?" Charles asked Johnny as they cleaned up for supper.

"We'll have to wait till after supper, I guess. You know Mama. But it must be something!" Johnny observed.

The meal was a gay one. Mama had prepared all the boys' favorite dishes. The family crowded the table, for the Ringling boys were all large fellows. And now they all were home, with the exception of Gus. Mama and Ida and Louise waited on their men-folk. Ida, a tall, lovely girl of nine, watched her brothers with adoring eyes. She hardly knew Albert, he had been away so

The meal was a gay one.

much, but she knew what he had been doing, and it sounded romantic.

Finally, in the midst of the dessert, Charles laid down his fork. "I can't eat another bite, Al, till you and Otto tell us what has brought you home."

Albert grinned at him across the table. "Make a guess, Charlie."

"You've joined a real circus, a big circus!" Charles guessed.

"Pretty close. I am going to start my own show!"

The words fell like a bomb among the younger boys. Alf T. and Charles, Johnny and Henry stared at Albert.

Charles was the first to get his voice.

"Take me, Al! Take me!" he begged eagerly.

Mama laid her hand on Charles' head. Her voice tried to be gay. "*Ja,* Charlie! He will take you. He wants to take you all!" She turned away toward the stove.

"Tell us about it. When will you start? What about your job?"

Albert held up his hand. "Listen! It won't take long. I'm like Papa, I guess. I hate to work for others. And I think I've served my training period, with the Hall and Long show winter before last, and my own little troupe last winter. But I had plenty of trouble with that troupe. They'd quit on me for any reason or no reason at all. I talked it over with Louise, and she said she was willing to let me try it. And I wrote Otto and outlined my plans, and he agreed to meet me here to talk it over with Papa and Mama——"

"Oh, Mama!" Charles interrupted, turning to his mother. "You said yes!"

"What else would I say? Albert, he is a man with a wife, no? He can do what seems to him best, and he feels it is best for him and his wife to do this."

"But us, Mama? Me? You said I could go?"

Mama sighed. Papa nodded. He said, "Yes, Charlie. We have agreed. You all can go with Albert in his show."

Charles pushed back his chair with such a bang that it tumbled over on the floor. He grabbed his mother and hugged her.

"But, listen, Charlie," Al shouted. "You haven't heard it all. I'm just going to have you boys—just the Ringlings. And we'll make Baraboo our headquarters—train here in the winter—travel in the summer——"

"Oh, Al, a real Ringling Brothers' Circus! I can't believe it. No more harness making. No more odd jobs. No more doing things we hate——"

Papa spoke softly, "You have been good boys and have not complained. But I knew that har-

ness making you hated all the time. Only Gus—
he is the only harness-maker son I have yet."

"Ringling Brothers!" Johnny chortled. Then,
suddenly, he asked, "What about Ida? You going to leave her out of it?"

Mama's arm went about the little girl. "You
bet he leaves Ida out of it. She, at least, I keep
with me."

"And I don't think Henry is ready yet for the
trouper's life. He's only thirteen. But later—if
he wants to come in with us——"

"I will, Al. You know I will," Henry cried.

"A circus! A Ringling Brothers' Circus!"
Charles repeated the happy words.

"Well—" Al hesitated—"I'm afraid I'll have
to change that a little bit, Charlie. We're not
ready for a real circus yet. We haven't the training or the money. But we can start with a musical troupe—a traveling concert troupe. You
boys have kept up with your music and are really

good musicians. We'll put some of the money we earn toward buying animals and talent and equipment."

"The old circus-box idea!" Otto put in.

"Yes, and I know who'll be in charge of that box," Charlie said, chuckling. He remembered how hard it had been to get Otto to spend their tent money for anything else.

"There's a lot to discuss," Albert said. He got up from the table. "We might as well begin making our plans right now."

2. *The Carnival of Wonders*

Charles Ringling had never been so excited in all his twenty-one years. He stood with Johnny across the street from the jail in Baraboo. He was staring at what, two days before, had been a vacant lot, overrun with weeds and rubbish.

"Look at it, Johnny!" he cried, his handsome

face flushed with happiness. "Just look at it, will you?"

"I am looking," Johnny answered. "I'm so happy I feel like turning a somersault right here in the street."

Charles chuckled. "That'd be a good way to advertise your clowning."

The two young men were admiring a tent—a real canvas tent that would seat at least six hundred people. From the top fluttered pennants of red, yellow and blue. Beside it stood a smaller tent, and back out of sight they knew there was a tiny dressing room. Across the big tent a streamer proclaimed in giant letters:

RINGLING BROTHERS' CARNIVAL OF NOVELTIES
AND MUSEUM OF LIVING WONDERS

Charles read the words softly and then said, "Today's the day. I'll bet Baraboo never forgets the nineteenth day of May, 1884. On that day the great Ringling Brothers' Circus was born."

Johnny grinned. "If you don't count last year when we *did* make pretty good money trouping. But this is our first tent show and it *is* quite a jump from our tiny tent like Joseph's coat and our little menagerie in Prairie du Chien," he admitted.

Otto and Alf T. crossed the street to join their brothers. Otto was frowning. He waved his hand toward the big tent.

"There's all our 'circus box' money—all we've earned in two years of trouping. And more. There's more than a thousand dollars tied up in those tents and the things in them."

"We'll get it all back," Alf T. said cheerfully. "It isn't the first time we've sunk every penny in a show, but we're still in business."

The parade that morning attracted a great deal of attention. A crowd gathered at the show grounds long before circus time that evening.

From outside Otto watched the line entering the tent, and a feeling of satisfaction replaced his former worry. But Alf T. saw from the performers' entry that the audience was crowding onto the blue-painted planks of the cheapest seats, while the more expensive reserved section was only comfortably full.

"Those lower blues are sagging, they're so packed," he whispered to Louise. Albert's wife stood beside him in her spangled, bareback rider's costume. She was holding the bridle of the big horse she would ride, ready to go into the ring.

Louise smiled. "I just hope this old farm horse doesn't stumble against them!"

The horse didn't stumble. But something worse happened. As Louise rode around the ring, standing gracefully on the horse's back, the crowd clapped and yelled. The weight and movement were too much for the bottom section of the loaded seats. A plank groaned. It sagged. Then with a screeching crack it broke and sent a score of screaming parents and children tumbling to the ground.

It was an awful moment. Albert and Otto ran to the broken benches. "Is anyone hurt?" they asked anxiously. No one was. Then Yankee Robinson, the old, out-of-work showman the boys had hired as ringmaster, stood up and shouted, "Well! Well! Well! Ain't that a great tumbling act for you? First time in any circus in Ameriky!"

They helped pick up the children, brushed them off, and said, "Now you go over to the reserved seats. There's room there. You'll be comfortable and safe—at no extra charge!"

Yankee Robinson said, "Now don't any more of you folks tumble down that way, or these Ringling boys will have to let you have the ring while they watch!"

The plank groaned and sagged, then broke.

The crowd chuckled good-naturedly. Those from the broken benches made their way to the reserved section, found seats and settled down.

The circus went on and the accident was soon forgotten.

In the smaller tent the side show did a rousing business. Baraboo had never seen such fine-sounding attractions. Alf T.'s love of big words had helped him to give elegant names to every exhibit. There were the Circassian snake charmer; the "Hideous Hyena Striata Gigantica," an ugly big striped hyena that Albert had bought from a traveling menagerie in St. Paul; an educated pig that would grunt answers to questions—sometimes; an extremely thin fellow billed as a skeleton man; and a magician who did card tricks and pulled the most surprising things out of a silk hat.

As soon as the evening show was over, all the performers became roustabouts. They went to work taking down the tents and loading them and the seats, the animals and the equipment into

the ten farm wagons the Ringlings had rented.
In the dark of the night they set out for their next
stand.

"We're on the road at last," Charles said. "Our
dream has come true, Johnny."

"Next stop Sauk City," Alf T. said, excitement
giving a ring to his quiet voice.

X

CIRCUS KINGS OF AMERICA

1. *The World's Greatest Show*

IN the middle of a hot August night in 1904, the Ringling Brothers' circus train pulled into Salt Lake City, Utah. There were fifty cars, all brightly painted red and yellow. Crowds of boys were at the siding when the cars stopped near the Fair Grounds.

They watched excitedly as the roustabouts unloaded canvas, poles and ropes. Heavy horses and huge elephants, acting with the precision of circus artists, stepped knowingly over the dry grass. They pulled a rope to raise a great section of canvas, or pushed a mammoth pole to support and tighten a tent top. The white canvas of the big top rose like magic.

When the sun rose, the lot was in order.

Watching the big top go up, the Salt Lake City boys paid scant attention as smaller tents were erected along a wide pathway. In front of each of these was hoisted a brilliant canvas sign with colored pictures. The pictures showed the attractions to be found inside. When the sun rose that summer morning the circus lot was in order. "The World's Greatest Show" was ready for the thousands who would visit it.

Charles Ringling—Mr. Charles, now—stood on the platform of the private car in which the five brothers traveled with their circus. Charles' handsome face was smiling.

"Look at them, John!" he exclaimed. "Boys haven't changed much since that morning in McGregor when we went down to the dock to watch Dan Rice's Circus unload."

"But what they see is a bit different from what we saw," John pointed out.

The boys were scattering now as they left for home and breakfast. But they would be back on Main Street at ten o'clock to see the parade.

It seemed as if everybody in Salt Lake City was waiting to greet the famous brothers as they rode at the head of the half-mile-long pageant. Their carriage was pulled by six perfectly matched white horses. They were easily recognized because a huge picture of the five Ringlings—Albert, Otto, Alf T., Charles and John—had been on the city's signboards for weeks.

A group of girl buglers followed the Ringling brothers' carriage. Then came brilliant red wagons, lavishly decorated in gold. The sides were open and barred to show the pacing animals within. The lions, tigers, leopards and gorillas were moving restlessly and glaring out at the shouting crowds. Other beautiful wagons carried bands on top. The bands played stirring airs that made the little girls along the street tap their feet in time to the music.

There were dozens of ladies in beautiful dresses and plumed hats riding on the famous "high-school horses" that stepped along dancingly to the gay tunes. These horses were so smart and clever that someone had said they acted as if they had been to high school, and the idea stuck. There were zebras and spotted ponies and camels. As each animal appeared the children shouted and clapped. But when the herd of elephants marched sedately by the youngsters were silent. There were twenty-six of these giant creatures. On the head of each rode a dark-skinned, curiously dressed man, who guided his steed with scarcely a movement.

All along, beside the wagons and horses, ran the clowns—some laughing, some crying, some tumbling, some riding little donkeys or stick horses.

Last of all came the calliope, shrilling its inviting music. Charles, at the head of the parade, couldn't hear the calliope. But he knew it was there, and it made him think of Dan Rice's circus boat, coming around the bend of the river, its steam whistle playing.

Back at the circus ground, Charles came up to Alf T. and handed him the early edition of the afternoon paper.

"You've done it, as usual." He grinned. "Front-page publicity. You've never missed since Prairie du Chien."

Alf T. took the paper. There, at the top of the first page, was a three-column "box" telling about the parade and the circus.

Alf T.'s eyes traveled over the story. "Listen to this." He chuckled. " 'The parade was a pageant never surpassed by any circus in this city. The Ringling brothers advertise the World's Greatest Show, and it is a claim difficult to combat. Even the Ringling brothers' calliope doesn't screech as untunefully as the calliopes of other circuses.' " That made them both laugh.

2. *A Golden Jubilee*

On another August day, twenty-nine years after the appearance in Salt Lake City, Baraboo, Wisconsin, was in a great state of excitement. The biggest event in its history was taking place. Thousands of visitors were thronging the streets. Among them were many famous people: the governor and a former governor of the state; senators and congressmen up from Washington; the president of the state university. Newspaper reporters and photographers were everywhere.

Baraboo was celebrating the golden jubilee of the Ringling Brothers' Circus. This year, 1933, climaxed fifty years of successful appearances. There were a thousand people in the show now, and a menagerie that cost a million dollars.

Papers all over the country carried stories about the event. On the front pages were pictures of the Ringlings who were being honored. Louise, Albert's widow, was seventy-eight years old now, but still a beauty. Ida, who had been the family baby, was pictured with her daughter Salome and her two sons, John Ringling North and Henry North. Of course there were portraits of the five famous brothers who had founded the circus. Sadly, none of them were present. Of all the seven brothers, only John was still alive, and he was ill at his beautiful home in Sarasota, Florida.

The governor of Wisconsin and the mayor of Baraboo sat on a platform that had been erected on Main Street. Beside them sat the members of the Ringling family, with a few close friends.

"Here they come!" someone shouted. The group on the platform leaned forward. Down Main Street marched a band, playing the tune that had opened every Ringling circus for nearly a third of a century: "The Stars and Stripes Forever!" Behind the band lumbered five elephants, entirely covered with gold paint in honor of the golden jubilee.

Young John Ringling North stared at them. "I wonder how many gallons of paint it took to cover them," he said to his brother, Henry.

Other bands, old circus wagons, performers who had worked for the famous brothers followed the elephants in a long procession.

The governor turned to the mayor. "We should send a telegram to John Ringling," he said. "He has doubtless received thousands today, but there should be one direct from the celebration."

A little later, in his Florida home, Mr. John read the dispatch: "Congratulations to the circus king of America on this golden jubilee from his old home state and his old home town."

"Congratulations to the circus king!"

He stared at the yellow paper. "Circus king! I never have deserved that title," he muttered. "Albert, yes, or Otto or Charles—any of us but me. I was just the clown."

He smiled, remembering the old days. He could almost hear the shouts and cheers that must be ringing along Baraboo's Main Street. "And five golden elephants!" He chuckled, recalling what he had been told in advance about the celebration. "How Charlie would have loved that!"